'I wish to purchase the Earl of Deversham,' the young lady said sweetly.

Nothing in her modish appearance suggested to Mr Horace Ponting, lawyer of the City of London in the year 1815, that Miss Dominga Romero-Browne had taken leave of her senses. Indeed, not only was she a vision of youth and beauty, but also endowed with a vast fortune.

But these attributes had no effect at all on the heart of Hugo, Earl of Deversham. Forced to marry for money, the wretched aristocrat's hand had been given to one woman while his heart still belonged to another.

Could the beautiful Dominga, once she became the Countess of Deversham, hope to win more than a title?

To Catch An Earl
Rosina Pyatt

MILLS & BOON LIMITED
London · Sydney · Toronto

First published in Great Britain 1982
by Mills & Boon Limited, 15–16 Brook's Mews,
London W1A 1DR

ISBN 0 263 73907 4

04/0782/

Set in 10 on 10 pt Linotron Times

Photoset by Rowland Phototypesetting Ltd
Bury St Edmunds, Suffolk
Made and printed in Great Britain by
Cox & Wyman Ltd, Reading

CHAPTER
ONE

'I WISH to purchase the Earl of Deversham,' the young lady said sweetly, smoothing a slight wrinkle from her gloves of finest lavender kid.

Mr Horace Ponting gasped. Few things had the power to rob him of speech, but this extraordinary utterance suspended his faculties entirely.

He blinked, hoping that when he looked again she would be gone. She was not. There she sat, languidly arranging her fashionable gown as if she were commissioning nothing more out of the way than a new bonnet. She was a vision of youth and beauty such as his office in the City of London had never seen before. A lady of quality. Such a preposterous statement could never have passed her genteel lips.

And so it was that Horace Ponting, celebrated though he was for the flair and discretion with which he had pulled off many a delicate business deal, was forced to distrust his ears. Damme, she hadn't even had the decency to wrap up the matter in clean linen. He must have misheard her.

'You—you wish to purchase the Earl of Deversham?' he faltered at last.

The young lady sighed. 'I thought I had made that perfectly plain. I want you to discover the Earl's price for taking me as his bride.'

So! There was the confirmation. It was not his wits that had gone a'begging but the young lady's. She was as mad as a March hare. Yet justice forced him to admit that there was nothing in her extremely modish appearance to suggest a hasty flight from Bedlam.

Amusement flickered in her eyes as she divined his thoughts. 'I grant that my commission is a trifle unusual, but it is not, surely, beyond the bounds of your comprehension?'

'A trifle unusual! You understate the case,' Mr Ponting

returned huffily. 'It is nothing less than insane.'

A thought crossed his mind and understanding dawned. He beamed.

'Ah, I have it, miss. This is a jape. Which of my rivals sent you here to make a fool of honest Horace Ponting? Well, you'll not do that, my pretty, no matter how early you come knocking at my door.'

That had to be it, he thought triumphantly. Now, who could have rigged her out as fine as fivepence to trap him into an indiscretion that would have enraged one of the haughtiest families in the land? It had to be one of his rivals. Somebody who wished to topple him from his throne as undisputed king of those who made a living in the warrens of the City.

Who was she, then, this girl? Or rather, what was she? An actress? A piece of Haymarket ware paid to alter her profession temporarily? If so, she was a most delectable item of merchandise. He was sure he could find a more profitable outlet for her charms.

These musings were doomed to a premature death. If limpid brown eyes could look frosty, he was being frozen where he sat. The young lady had read his mind again. The raising of her eyebrows was slight, but such was the hauteur it conveyed that Mr Ponting was forced into a rapid re-appraisal of her.

Decidedly not a loose woman, he thought, yet she could not be a lady of quality. As such, she would have no need of his services as an intermediary. Those who moved in exalted circles did their own matchmaking.

A rich merchant's daughter, perhaps? Yet even the most vulgar of tradesmen seeking an aristocratic match for his daughter would have the sense to see to the business himself.

And the Earl of Deversham as prey, no less! The very cream of the aristocracy. Badly in debt, to be sure, but starched-up enough to be utterly unassailable to the schemes of this young lady, whoever she might be.

What had she called herself? Miss Brown? That alone was suspicious. And why should an unknown Miss Brown dare to look as high as Deversham?

Mr Ponting revised what he knew about that august

family. It was little enough. Aristocracy did not mix with the Pontings of this world.

There had been rumours in the City after the recent death of the sixth Earl, however. That nobleman had been credited with completing the ruin of the family fortunes which had been started by the fourth Earl and worsened by the fifth. Whisper had it that creditors were scrabbling for payment. The new Earl must be properly in the basket, poor chap, but marriage to a rich Society lady would doubtless remedy that. Deversham had an ancient and illustrious title to offer, after all, and his country seat in Hampshire was said to be second to none.

Mr Ponting, knowing the workings of the aristocratic world as this shameless beauty most clearly did not, was more suspicious than ever. He must not let hauteur confuse him. Miss Brown must be an actress.

He wagged a chubby finger at her. 'I know you're here to make a fool of me. Who sent you? Come now, confess, and we'll have a cosy laugh together.'

She thought he was becoming tedious. Her tapping foot conveyed her irritation.

'I am not in the mood for laughter and I know of no jape. Neither do I understand why you are making such a fuss of a simple business deal. I wish you to discover Deversham's bride price. You must be aware there is a price for everything, even a coronet.'

She paused to give Mr Ponting time to contradict her. When he did not, she continued: 'This commission is not beyond your ability. I did not pick your name out of a hat. I have it on the best authority that your flair in these matters is exceptional. Your discretion, also, is something of a byword in the City.'

Such an appreciation of his talents would have gratified Mr Ponting at any other time, but he could not shake the feeling that he was being made a laughing stock.

'The very idea is preposterous!' he exclaimed.

'I think not,' she replied. 'Even if it were, the preposterous can be reduced to the commonplace if one contrives sufficiently. And I shall contrive. I shall become the Countess of Deversham with or without your aid. So tell me, are you with me or not?'

'No,' snapped Mr Ponting.

'Very well.' The grace with which the young lady stood up evoked admiration even in Mr Ponting's plump chest.

She picked up her reticule and long-handled parasol. 'It is a pity we did not get as far as discussing your remuneration for acting as my intermediary,' she said.

'It's all a hum and I'd be an idiot not to know it,' Mr Ponting replied severely. 'My business will be better off without your commission, young lady.'

'I must congratulate you. You must indeed be successful. Five hundred guineas is not to be whistled down the wind without a second thought.'

Mr Ponting, who was rising to escort this strange damsel from his chamber, was arrested halfway. 'Five hundred guineas?' he exclaimed.

'One hundred for securing an interview for me with the Earl. Another four hundred when his ring is upon my finger. Excessively generous, you must own, but I am not one to haggle over the achievement of an ambition. Nor would I dream of underpricing your exceptional talents,' she added dulcetly.

The bait was before Mr Ponting, overwhelmingly tempting. He yearned to swallow it, along with his natural caution. He came round his desk, clasped her arm and gently pressed her back into her chair. 'Let me think,' he begged.

He crossed the polished floor of his office, opened the door and looked out. His two clerks were perched on their high stools, busily scrawling into their ledgers. They did not even look up as their master scrutinised them.

Satisfied, Mr Ponting closed the door firmly. It was with a somewhat conspiratorial air that he returned to his desk. He was too agitated, however, to sit down.

He said worriedly: 'Respectability is the pillar upon which my business is built. Not for any sum would I endanger that.'

It was nothing less than the truth. His offices in the City might not be so very far from the back-slums of Westminster's Tothill Fields, but the distance could not be measured in miles alone. He had no wish to find himself discredited to the point where he was back collecting rents in those seedy tenements. He had striven too hard and too long for these desirable rooms in the City.

He felt the need to underline his agitation. 'You must understand that I cannot afford to have my name connected with anything shady.'

'Naturally,' she returned dryly. 'Neither can I. Grant me the wit not to attempt to assail an aristocratic—er—citadel from any but the most respectable quarter.'

'We are at one on that,' he muttered fervently. 'I don't know, though. Deversham, indeed! I've never flown that high before . . . might come a cropper . . . five hundred guineas, eh? It tempts . . . it most certainly tempts . . .'

The young lady seemed to have no trouble making sense of these disjointed utterances. 'Nobody could accuse you of acting on any but the very best of intentions,' she soothed him, 'and the venture will be successful.'

'I wish I had your faith. But the Earl! You would need a dowry the size of Deversham Hall itself, and no mistake, to get so much as a glance from that direction.'

'I think it is time I put my cards on the table,' the beauty said decisively. 'At least, one card.'

She opened her reticule and produced a gold cardholder. From it she drew a small piece of paste-board. She handed it to him.

Mr Ponting studied the name elegantly inscribed in gold upon it. 'Miss Dominga Romero-Browne,' he said aloud.

What an odd name, to be sure. It meant nothing to him. Nor did the address: Chersey Manor, Surrey.

She said: 'My father was Wilfrid Browne. That will explain a great deal to you.'

It did. It most certainly did. Though not a name that any member of the *ton* would be familiar with, no man of business could deny having heard of so magnificent an entrepreneur as Wilfrid Browne. He was a model of what could be achieved by diligent, if not always scrupulous, endeavour. There was scarcely a money-making pie in the length and breadth of the realm that had not had at least one of Wilfrid Browne's avaricious fingers in it.

Browne—when had the 'e' been added? Mr Ponting wondered—had been a master of turning a penny into a pound, a pound into a hundred, and a hundred into count-less thousands.

No wonder this young lady was behaving as if she was as rich as Croesus. Word had circulated the City on the unlamented demise of Wilfrid Browne that a hitherto unknown daughter had reaped the benefit of his mercenary connivings.

This, presumably, was that fortunate daughter.

As Browne had always been tight-mouthed about his personal life, Mr Ponting had to voice his puzzlement: 'Romero-Browne?'

'My mother was a Spanish gentlewoman and very proud of her lineage. My dear papa gratified her by joining her name to his when they were wed,' Dominga replied, with-out a grain of truth. She had inherited more than money from her wily father.

'I see,' Mr Ponting could not quite reconcile himself to the idea of Wilfrid Browne gratifying anybody, but he continued: 'It was your father's wish that you married into the aristocracy?'

'His dearest wish.' Dominga did not lie this time. Her father's plotting towards that end had begun before she first opened her lustrous eyes upon the world. That was why the name she bore was the same as the one respectably recorded in the parish register of the northern village where she had been born. If Wilfrid Browne had never been quite above question himself, he had done his cunning best to ensure that his daughter would always be. He had been the master of the long-term plan.

Like a small dog worrying at an over-large bone, Mr Ponting burst out: 'But why the Earl of Deversham? Would not a baronet—?'

'No,' replied Dominga unequivocally.

'An émigré French aristocrat?'

'Certainly not.'

'An Irish earl, then?'

'Deversham. None other.'

'Good gracious, miss, you might as well set your cap at a duke!'

'I might,' she agreed calmly. 'However, it is to be Dever-sham.'

'So adamant! You must have a reason.'

'I do not think you need to concern yourself with that,' Dominga reproved gently.

He thought he should, but it would clearly be to no avail. 'I might be able to gain the Earl's ear if I grease the right palms,' he admitted grudgingly. 'But what then? I have no wish to be thrown out into the street.'

'You will not be. Let us be vulgar, Mr Ponting, and discuss money. I have two hundred thousand pounds at my immediate disposal. The rest of my principal is invested in Funds and industry to ensure me a yearly income of not less than twenty thousand pounds. Possibly double that figure, depending on investment returns from many sources.'

Mr Ponting whistled soundlessly.

'Quite so,' Dominga said. 'There's not an heiress in the country to match me. The day the Earl makes me his Countess, he will be fifty thousand pounds the richer. In addition, he will receive a yearly sum from me, the details of which we can settle between us.'

'But will not your fortune go to your husband on your marriage?' asked Mr Ponting, for that was the usual practice.

Dominga smiled sweetly. 'No. My father left a most precise Will. My fortune will always be in my hands.'

'The Earl won't care for that. 'Tis well known women have no head for money matters.'

'This head has, Mr Ponting. I could balance a ledger before I could set a stitch in a sampler. However, the dowry I am offering is not to be sniffed at, even by an earl.'

'You don't know how puffed-up is the family you wish to marry into,' fretted Mr Ponting.

'I know the present Earl has not a feather to fly with, and that's a great deal more to the point. He is not in a position to refuse my offer.'

'I wonder?' Mr Ponting tapped the side of his nose with a nervous finger. 'Will you grant me a few minutes' private thought? No, I don't wish you to leave the room. Just be silent for a while, if you will be so good. I need to concentrate.'

Since Miss Romero-Browne inclined her head graciously, he walked to the window. He stood there, hands clasped behind him, corpulent stomach thrust out, head bowed in thought.

Could it be done? Could it really be done?

He believed there was much in what Miss Romero-Browne said. He could not like her name, though, and was very sure the Earl would not. Part foreign and part common.

Mr Ponting turned to peer at her covertly. No matter, perhaps. Beauty such as hers had been known to overcome worse obstacles. That vivid colouring, so exotic to an English eye, was no doubt inherited from her Spanish mother.

He turned back to the window and looked down into the narrow street. He watched idly as a ragged urchin swept a crossing through the filth so that a frock-coated merchant could gain the other side of the street without soiling his polished boots. A man with a tray of hot pies on his head cried out his wares, jostling for space with a hawker of rat traps. A hackney carriage rattled past, the noise of its wheels on the cobbles almost obliterating the shrill sounds of a squabble in progress farther along the street.

The City of London, in that momentous year of 1815, was much loved by Horace Ponting. It was his pride, his passion, his reason for being. Its squalor, however, frequently offended his nose, particularly at this time of year when the heat made everything rot that much faster.

The stench rose to his nostrils now, even though it was early in the day. By noon it would be intolerable and this window, open to let in a light July breeze, would have to be closed.

A beggar passed by, one hand missing, an alms bowl held in the other. From the set of his shoulders and upright carriage he did not look like an old man, though one eye was covered by a patch and much of his face was obscured by unkempt hair. He wore a ragged coat of scarlet cloth. A proud soldier once, then. Now, presumably, a victim of Napoleon's lust for power. In which battle had he received such disfigurements?

Corunna, Talavera, Vittoria? There had been so many . . . and such were their outlandish names that they found no ready niche in an Anglo-Saxon memory. They were forgotten almost as soon as the soldiers who had fought in them.

But the shadow of Napoleon, much to Mr Ponting's satisfaction, no longer covered Europe and challenged England. It had been vanquished last month by the battle named after the Belgian village of Waterloo, and London Town had gone wild with joy at such a glorious victory.

Soon the inglorious results of that stirring blood-bath would be visible below Mr Ponting's window. New cripples would be begging in the streets.

At first their bright coats would bring generous response, then people would begin to grumble again at the shocking rise in the cost of living caused by the wars with the French. Their gratitude towards their gallant heroes would fade with the soldiers' coats. Winning battles was a tradition. Caring for its casualties was not.

Well, that was life. Harsh, but worth the struggle none-the-less. Otherwise, why did destitute cripples beg as a means of sustaining life instead of lying down to die? So reasoned Mr Ponting.

But these thoughts and observations skimmed only over the surface of his mind, as if to shield the real problem with which his brain was grappling. Deep, delicate stuff this, as he explored ways through the maze of pitfalls that might separate Miss Romero-Browne from the Deversham coronet, and himself from five hundred guineas.

For such a prize the young lady was prepared to hazard much. So, too, would he . . . if he could satisfy himself it could be done.

His thoughts were crystallising and he began to plot in earnest. So much, naturally, depended on the young lady herself. Deversham could not take her money and lock her up in a turret, which was not unknown in medieval times.

In this enlightened age, however, there must be nothing about Miss Romero-Browne which could offend Society's fastidious eye.

Mr Ponting closed the window, shutting out the smell and the noise, and turned to study her anew.

His initial impression of her had most decidedly been of a young lady who moved in the first circles, and he was not easily deceived. His later suppositions had been based on the nature of her business, not on her appearance. This was of paramount importance if she were to be foisted on the Earl, and so he studied her carefully.

No blush stained the maiden's cheek, although she could not but be aware of his scrutiny. No doubts or modesty made her fidget and cast down her beautiful eyes. Hopefully, the Earl would misinterpret this as the natural assurance of a lady, never suspecting the brazenness of it all.

So far, so good. The crêpe walking dress of palest lavender which she wore had just one modest flounce at the hem, the inspired understatement of a modiste who clearly knew all about dressing fashionable young maidens. The lavender bonnet upon her head was adorned with an ostrich feather which curled becomingly towards her face. Her lavender slippers, gloves, reticule and parasol were all the proper trappings of a gently-reared girl. The final impression she gave was of expense without ostentation. There was nothing vulgar about her to disgust the most critical of minds which, in this instance, Mr Ponting's was.

She had style—and courage, too. With five daughters of his own, Mr Ponting knew well that such a shade of lavender was generally considered the prerogative of ladies with fair hair and pale colouring. Miss Romero-Browne apparently disagreed, and magnificently so. She bloomed in a colour which should have looked insipid upon her.

Mr Ponting turned his attention on her dazzling face, studying each feature in turn, searching for some fatal flaw. He found none. There was no squint in her large brown eyes. No coarseness marred her ivory complexion. No rouge was added to her high cheekbones. Nor did the gloss and colour of her jet-black hair owe anything to the jars and pots so many ladies were forced to resort to.

As for her frame, she was built on Junoesque lines. No frail, wilting beauty this. Her high-waisted gown had trouble concealing the generous lines of her lithe body.

She was as perfect as any man could wish and would undoubtedly cut a dash, even if she failed to snare the Earl.

Yet she must not fail, since he had five hundred guineas dangling on the outcome. That was a thought to warm himself by as he weaved plans to get her legally into the Earl's bed.

Anxiety brought his eyebrows down. Her voice. It had impressed him, had it not? Yes, certainly. Soft, well-modulated, with a fascinating hint of huskiness. Had he missed the ruinous overtones of a brogue? He profoundly hoped not. She must not offend the Earl's ear any more than she did his eye. He must encourage her to talk, hopefully unguardedly.

'There are some questions of a personal nature I must ask, Miss Romero-Browne, if we are to pursue this—er—quest. I have your permission?'

'Certainly. I expect you to ask many.'

What a cool customer she was, but his frown cleared. Her voice was definitely all that a lady's should be and, moreover, she was not going to be missish.

The intricate web through which he must guide her was beginning to look less formidable. Really, one must take one's hat off to old Browne. He had had his daughter admirably schooled.

'Your age?' he began.

'Seventeen.' Her teeth gleamed in a smile. 'I am just out of the schoolroom. Although my father died six months ago there was a period of strict mourning to be observed. He had this scheme in hand before his demise and directed me to you to bring it to a conclusion.'

'Aaah . . .' Mr Ponting allowed himself to feel flattered this time. 'Your father's death was not sudden, I take it? There was time to enlighten you on what he had in mind?'

'Yes.' For a moment Dominga was not seeing Mr Ponting's well-fed face but older, thinner features with deeply-lined cheeks, sharp grey eyes and a thick thatch of white hair. Dearest Papa to her; 'that demon Browne' to others.

'Inflammation of the lungs, I heard?' Mr Ponting pursued delicately.

'Yes. It began with a cold that would not clear.' A smile, half-rueful and half-proud, crossed her face. 'My father was ever a law unto himself. He would heed no advice. By the time he took to his bed he was very ill. He was sixty-seven, but he did not seem so old to me.'

Dominga paused, then added: 'The years had touched his face but not clouded his mind. His only regret was that he could not see me safely through this business before . . . before . . .'

Her grief was real. She had adored her father.

'Quite so,' said Mr Ponting hastily, but she presented a wholly unrecognisable side of Wilfrid Browne. Human, and who would have thought it? That old rascal a doting father? Capable of sireing and rearing such a ravishing daughter? He must have led a dual life with dual faces, and nobody any the wiser.

But Mr Ponting would not allow himself to be diverted. He came to the point which really baffled him. 'Why Deversham, miss? I cannot understand why your father selected him. That's flying devilishly high.'

Long black lashes swept down to conceal Dominga's eyes. 'He did not select him. I did.'

'Indeed?' A rosy vision of romance was conjured up in Mr Ponting's bemused brain. He saw this choice young damsel, rich but blighted by plebeian birth, setting her eyes on a dashing young blade and losing her heart to him.

But he—Deversham—was so elevated by birth that he was beyond her reach. What could she do, this daughter of a man part-merchant and part-pirate? Why, the only thing. She had turned to her father and he, who could deny her nothing, had begun to plot as only he knew how.

A sigh escaped Mr Ponting. To think that he had been selected by the awe-inspiring Wilfrid Browne to take on the mantle of Cupid, albeit with a quiver of gold rather than arrows. What did that matter? The principle was the same.

He felt more reconciled towards the role he was about to play. It suited his temperament to believe he was smoothing the path of true love. Again he brought himself back to the business at hand. 'Your mother, Miss Romero-Browne?'

'Dead, alas, before I was in leading-strings.'

'Who chaperons you?'

'My step-mama.'

'A respectable lady?' Mr Ponting had to be blunt.

'Unquestionably. A minister's sister. She's a Reverson, cousin to Sir Piers Reverson. My father married her when I was two years old, so she has always had the care of me.'

'Her temperament, character and aims?'

'She is quiet and kindly. A retiring lady who weaves her life around the Manor and our little village. She would be loath to leave it.'

Mr Ponting's double chin quivered with approval. That was very good. He had feared a socially-aspiring woman who would thrust herself upon Deversham in the reprehensible manner of the shabby-genteel, causing trouble when she was repulsed.

'Your real mother was Spanish, you say? And gentry?'

'Yes,' lied Dominga, her eyes never wavering from Mr Ponting's face.

'You're sure?'

'Indubitably. So sad I never knew her . . .' Dominga's voice was full of tragic overtones as it trailed away.

Mr Ponting was completely deceived, and he strove to cheer her up.

'Come, come, Miss Romero-Browne. Do not fall into a fit of the dismals. Much is working in your favour. A Spanish lady for a mother, a rich father, respectable relations and great personal beauty. Perhaps, after all, it will not be impossible to bring you to your heart's desire.'

CHAPTER
TWO

AFTER these bracing words, Mr Ponting fell silent. He was
busy with his thoughts again and Dominga had cause to be
busy with hers.

She had been reared to think of herself as the daughter of
a Spanish lady, and had never doubted it. Nor had she
doubted that one day she would be, as Papa promised, a
great lady in her own right. Indeed, her father's pet name
for her had been Milady. That was not an acknowledge-
ment of her imperious little ways, but an admission of his
high ambition for her.

Dominga had believed his intentions to marry her to a
title, of which she thoroughly approved, had sprung from
her mother being 'gentry'. Rich as he was, certain doors
had always been closed to him. They would open for his
daughter. She would rub shoulders with the highest in the
land. All she had to do was mind her lessons, listen to his
counsel, understand the power of money and the value of
patience.

Mostly, Dominga was as dutiful as he could have wished.
But not always. There was a wild and wilful streak in her
which had caused Wilfrid, understanding her better than
she did herself, to have her closely guarded. Within the
house she was watched by her step-mama, her governess
and maid. Outside, a burly manservant dogged her footsteps. But, when one of her overwhelming moods of restlessness seized her, Dominga had always managed to
escape to wander freely on her own. When she returned,
she bore the storm that burst over her head stoically, in
some strange way satisfied by her hours of freedom, so that
she would be no trouble for months to come. Until the next
time.

And it was of the last time, her final escapade, that

Dominga was thinking as she sat quietly in Mr Ponting's office.

She had been fifteen. Bursting with life, mischief and new-found womanhood. It was in this state of quivering expectancy for she knew not what, that she had crossed the path of milords Harry and Hugo Huntsleigh, twin sons of the fifth Earl of Deversham.

God-like, they had seemed to her in their fair-haired handsomeness.

Man-like, one of them had seduced her. To this day, she did not know which, for looking at them was like having double vision.

It was not the fact that she had been seduced that had made Dominga burn with anger these three years past. She was honest enough to admit she had merely been supplied with what she had been unconsciously seeking. No, it was what had happened afterwards that had seared her pride, wounded her imperious spirit, until nothing less than marrying one of them—the one with the title, naturally—would appease her.

As her father had drummed into her, debts had to be paid. And the squirming shame that had been inflicted upon her on that momentous day could only be repaid in kind. Dominga intended to exact it in full.

One twin, Harry, had become the sixth Earl of Deversham within days of her humiliation. Well, he had come to a sudden end and was beyond her reach. But the other twin, Hugo, was not. He was now the seventh Earl—her quarry. From him she would have her coronet and her revenge.

Dominga had trouble containing her elation now that she was so near to her goal. And then she breathed deeply, remembering another kind of elation which she had felt so wonderfully and briefly on that never-to-be-forgotten day.

It had been late one fine October afternoon when she had stolen silently from her books and her watchdogs to run headlong through the home wood. For a while, her freedom had been enough but, when that palled, she had wandered down to the village. She had gone into the yard of the inn, and found it in a turmoil. Molly, the young and rather simple-minded chambermaid, was rushing towards the back door with a large jug of milk.

'Lawks, Miss Dominga,' she had exclaimed, stopping short, 'a fine time you pick to come a'visiting. 'Tis like a nest of wasps has been stirred up inside, what with the hustle and bustle and the running this way and that.'

She set down the milk jug to add suspiciously: 'Where's Gibbons? Don't tell me you've run off alone again. We've trouble enough.'

'Never mind about Gibbons,' Dominga replied. 'What is happening?'

'Two lords are putting up with us, Miss Dominga, all unexpected-like. They were travelling post from Leicester where they've been a'hunting because it seems the Earl, their father, is about to slip his wind. Howsoever, the chaise is broken and can't be fixed afore tomorrow.'

'But why are they putting up here?' Dominga asked. 'This is no posting inn.'

'And ain't I grateful for it, for I disremember ever seeing such fuss and pother! What with them wanting the linen in their bedchambers changed because they suspicion the sheets already on the beds, and having Mr Mellors turn his cellars upside down looking for wine he's never heard of, and expecting fine and dandy food from Mrs Mellors which she don't know hardly how to cook, and me being sent all over the village on errands with them beds not made yet, 'tis like a madhouse.'

Dominga, dismissing this domestic trivia as beneath her, demanded: 'What are they like, these lords?'

Molly's harassed expression was replaced by a beatific beam. 'Oh, Miss Dominga! As aristocratic as you could wish, and ever so fancy. Twins they are, and such handsome men as I never expect to see again.'

She giggled, blushed and went on: 'Lusty young men, too. My bottom's fair black and blue with the pinching, and them not been here above a half hour. Not that I'd have the heart to deny them. I tell you straight, young as you are, you'd be all a'twitter if you was to clap eyes on them, so it's just as well you won't.'

Dominga's chin jutted slightly: 'It isn't fair that you should have all the fun when nothing exciting ever happens to me. I will see them! My mind is quite made up.'

Molly's eyes rounded. 'Bless you, Mrs Mellors would

never let you near them frisky young bucks, not with you being gently-born and her so afeard of your father.'

But Dominga was thinking. 'You were talking of changing the beds. Well, then, I shall help you. I shall be a chambermaid. You must sneak me up to your room, Molly, and loan me some of your clothes.'

'Miss Dominga, I wouldn't dare! The Mellors would kill me.'

'Since one is in the cellar and the other in the kitchen, they won't know,' Dominga pointed out. 'Come, Molly, don't be such a spoilsport. You know how hedged-in I am all the time.'

Molly did, and felt sorry for her, but not sorry enough to override her fear of her employers. 'I wouldn't dare,' she reiterated. 'Truly, I wouldn't.'

'Molly,' replied Dominga severely, 'if you don't help me I shall tell Mrs Mellors how I saw you coming out of the barn last week with young Tom. You know as well as I do she wants more than a chambermaid for a daughter-in-law. One hint in her ear of your little love-nest and she'll turn you off, anyway.'

'You're not supposed to know about such things!' Molly exclaimed, aghast. Then: 'You wouldn't tell, though? You couldn't.'

'I could,' Dominga promised her.

'I never would have thought it of you,' Molly grumbled, then capitulated. 'Oh, all right, then. No harm will come of it, I suppose, since I'll be with you.'

Giggling like conspirators, the girls crept up the back stairway to Molly's tiny attic where Dominga discarded her prim, high-necked and long-sleeved gown, slipped on one of Molly's and found herself transformed:

Her young breasts, which she had never taken much notice of, suddenly seemed startling, exposed as they were by the low-cut neckline Molly favoured. And her hair, freed from its ribands, curled waywardly from under the mobcap Molly thrust on her head.

When the maid stepped back to survey her handiwork, her eyes almost popped out of her head. 'Lawks, miss, you look as old as I am, and that's seventeen come Christmas.'

'Do I?' asked Dominga delightedly, wishing there was a mirror in the room.

'Yes, and you'll get more than you bargained for if those young gentlemen spot you in that rig. You don't know what you're doing.'

'Don't I?' Dominga grinned impishly at her. 'Then let's find out.'

'You are a handful,' Molly replied, half-admiringly and half-fearfully, 'but since the gentlemen are in the parlour I don't see what can go amiss. I'll let you have a peek at them when we've done the beds. Just a peek, mind.'

She led Dominga down the attic stairs to the landing and paused before one of the bedchambers. Before she could lift the latch, Mrs Mellors called: 'Molly, what are you doing up there? And where's the milk? Leave the beds and come here this instant. It's eggs I'm needing now and right sharpish.'

'Whatever shall I do?' Molly whispered.

Dominga gave her a little shove towards the stairs. 'As you are told, of course. If she comes up here we'll both be in the basket.'

'Run back to my room, then,' Molly said. 'I'll be back as quick as I can.'

She disappeared downstairs. Dominga, unwilling to let her adventure end so tamely, unlatched the bedchamber door and walked in. She pulled up short.

Molly had been wrong about the gentlemen being in the parlour. One of them was sprawled out on the bed, his modishly-attired form looking totally out of place on the homely patchwork quilt.

Without opening his eyes he drawled lazily: 'So there is some service in this curst place. If you are not too ham-fisted, you can take off my boots.'

Dominga, closing the door behind her and advancing to the bed, saw that he was as handsome as Molly had promised. She bobbed a curtsy and, adopting Molly's broad accent, replied: 'I'd be pleased and honoured, sir.'

The eyes opened. They were grey, and they filled with admiration as they scrutinised Dominga. 'It seems,' he said, propping himself up on one elbow, 'that this place is not as awful as I'd imagined.'

Dimples appeared in Dominga's cheeks and she curtsied again. Her left hand was taken and studied.

'No wedding band, either,' he added. 'The lads in this village must be blind.'

And with a quick flick of his wrist he pulled her on to the bed. Dominga collapsed across him with a flutter of petticoats and a small startled shriek. Her mobcap fell on the floor so that her black hair fell about her shoulders. She was expertly turned over on her back and then the young man was leaning over her, smiling.

Dominga smiled back. Why not tease him a little, as Molly would have done? She could always extricate herself if things became too playful. Meanwhile, she could enjoy this novel thrill of a dashing young blade finding her desirable. 'Struth, he even thought her old enough to be married . . .

He murmured: 'Beauty should always be saluted, particularly when it is encountered in unlikely places. How lucky you are to have a Huntsleigh to pay you fitting service.'

Dominga was just discovering what pleasure there could be in having strong arms close around her when the door opened. The gentleman frowned and turned his head to see who had intruded on him uninvited.

The frown disappeared. 'Damn it, brother, you have devilish timing,' he complained.

'And you,' replied his mirror image, closing the door and walking into the room to stare down at Dominga, 'have the most devilish luck.'

'Don't I just,' said the grey-eyed gentleman complacently, but tightening his hold on Dominga.

'Spin you for her,' suggested his twin casually, taking a coin from his pocket.

The arms holding Dominga loosened slightly as the grey-eyed twin looked from her to the coin.

'It's your proud boast that you never refuse a bet,' persisted the other, tossing the coin and clapping his hand over it. 'What's it to be?'

'Heads.'

The hand was removed from the coin. 'Tails it is. How appropriate. My—er—trick, brother.'

Dominga was still recovering from her surprise at seeing such identical twins, and her indignation at becoming the object of a bet, when the bed creaked as one brother replaced the other.

She now had blue eyes looking into hers, the only difference she could perceive between them. The door clicked shut and they were alone.

'This,' she began, then paused as she recollected that she must use Molly's accent, 'ain't what I'm used to, sir.'

'I'm profoundly glad to hear it,' said the blue-eyed twin. 'A Huntsleigh would be mortified to be equated with a local stallion.'

Dominga was carefully thinking her way through this when firm lips closed on hers and coherent thought suddenly became extremely difficult. So this was why Molly risked Mrs Mellors' wrath by going into the barn with young Tom. She couldn't, she really couldn't, blame her.

As those pleasure-giving lips strayed from her lips to her ear and down to her throat, she wondered hazily if now was the time to finish her adventure. But then the lips were on her shoulders and she thought: *Just a little longer. If he thinks me grown up I mustn't act the child. I don't feel a child. Besides, I can always scream . . .*

She never did. Instead she dissolved into quivering anticipation as experienced hands explored her body. At some point Molly's mobcap was joined by her clothes upon the floor, but Dominga could only be grateful. They had got into the way so.

She remembered whispering: 'Are you my lord Harry or my lord Hugo?'

Only to be told: 'In such adventures, we never tell. Parental wrath wavers before a dual target. But do not worry, my sweet. You will be amply rewarded.'

His lips had covered Dominga's, then, and so urgently that she couldn't follow through the implications of what he had said. Couldn't, and didn't want to. Not at that moment.

It all seemed so terribly natural to her. The kisses leading to caresses. The caresses leading to the wild burst of lust and, finally, to exhaustion and satisfaction.

She had curled up, sated, quite delirious with happiness. She was totally obsessed with her own sensations and she scarcely noticed that the blue-eyed gentleman was clothing himself.

Dimly she wondered why she had ever imagined that young maidens were guarded so carefully against men, when clearly it was themselves they needed protecting from. She giggled slightly, very much in the manner of Molly. How much she had learnt today.

The young man, shrugging himself into his beautifully tailored coat, looked down at her. Appreciatively. She was so abandoned to the moment that she still lay naked on the patchwork quilt.

'Had you told me you were a virgin,' he said, 'I would have spent more time on you—although I vow you're not disappointed.'

Dominga's brain, which had been suspended by the demands her body made under the tuition of his skilful hands, began to tick over. She looked up at him, not knowing quite what she had expected. A betrothal, perhaps. His powerful arms about her again, lovingly, now that his lust was spent.

What she got was ten golden guineas showered over her. 'A handsome reward, you will agree, but a fair one. Virgins are rare, even in rural parts.'

Dominga looked at the guineas as if she had been betrayed. Then she glared at him, indignation quivering in her voice as she exclaimed: 'How dare you! I am a lady!'

He gave a shout of laughter. 'A woman now, certainly. Shall I send my brother up? Mayhap he'll double your earnings.'

'Go away,' she ground out with loathing, belatedly covering her nakedness by clutching the quilt about her. 'Go away.'

Instead he came towards her, and lifted her chin with a careless finger. Don't worry, my lovely. It's always the same with virgins. Begging to be bedded, then sorry afterwards. You will get over it.'

'Go away,' she repeated.

'Willingly, but first I'll give you some advice. Find a husband for yourself. You will be wanting satisfaction again, and shortly, for I vow your blood is as hot as any man's.'

He laughed again, and left her. It was the laugh, coupled with the dreadful golden guineas, that brought the burning shame to Dominga. She had not been raped. She knew that. But she had given herself totally to this man, had been ready to love him for ever, only to be tossed aside like some unwanted toy.

She crept from the bed and dressed herself quickly. Gathering up the guineas, for nobody must guess what had happened to her, she stole silently up to the attic.

As she dressed in her own clothes, she decided to tell Molly that she had changed and gone home as soon as she had been left alone. Molly would believe that. Certainly she would not believe that Miss Dominga Romero-Browne could have been seduced without screaming the inn down . . .

Like a wraith she made her way down the back stairs, across the yard and into the woods. Fortunately, her father was away on one of his numerous business trips. But only when her mortification had turned by degrees into a thirst for revenge could Dominga even face herself again in the mirror. She knew her weakness now—her own sensuality.

In the future, she vowed, she would always master it. Never would she forget what had happened when it had mastered her.

With her father's cunning and guile running apparently undiluted in her veins, Dominga had told him on his return that she had chanced to sight the Huntsleigh twins when they had put up in the village. Since one of them would be the Earl of Deversham one day, did Papa not think he would make a suitable husband for her? Such fair-haired handsomeness, she said, would wonderfully set off her own dark beauty.

Papa had said he would look into it, and so he had. Discovering that the Deversham finances were in an interesting state, he put that family at the top of his list of possible connections for his daughter.

Dominga, knowing her Papa and how well he could plot, had been satisfied. Yet it had not been until a few days before her father's death that she had learned the truth about the other blood that coursed through her, the fiery and unpredictable strain.

Dominga had been sitting beside his bed, engaged in turning for him the pages of a heavy ledger which he could not be persuaded to relinquish until what was literally his last gasp.

The quiet of the room had been broken only by his laboured breathing until he had said suddenly: 'It will all work out for you as I have planned, Milady, but I'll not leave anybody with a weapon to use against you. You shall have the truth.'

'What truth, Papa?' Dominga asked.

'About you. We both know it's convenient to lie upon occasion—that's bred in your blood and I've nurtured it—but the only safety lies in knowing the whole truth about any situation. Then you are prepared and can deflect a blow that might be aimed against you. No general advances with a flank exposed, not if he wants victory. He don't retreat without a rearguard, either.'

'What is this?' teased Dominga, amused. 'I don't have to enlist to get my coronet, do I?'

'You may laugh, you little scamp, but you'll be engaged in some rough skirmishing before you're mistress of Deversham Hall, and I'll not be here to see you safely through it.'

He paused, then added gruffly: 'Time's running out for me.'

Dominga bit her lip. 'I am what you have made of me, and something of you will live on as long as I do.'

'Aye, but don't interrupt me. I must tell you about your mother.'

'But I know all about her!' Dominga exclaimed, startled.

'What you know is mere fantasy. The Romero part of your name don't mean a thing. I dreamed it up before the wedding lines were signed, though, so it's recorded on your birth notice all nice and legally.'

'But Romero was my mother's name!'

Wilfrid shook his head. 'It's the truth, Milady, that I'm giving you. My last protection for you. You'll be the stronger for knowing what's fact and what's no more than a bag of moonshine.'

His dry voice, troubled by spasms of coughing, filled Dominga's wondering ears and fired her imagination. It also helped her understand why her passion had been so readily aroused by my lord Huntsleigh. Harry or Hugo . . . whichever had the much-remembered blue eyes.

When at last her father's voice ceased, Dominga stared at him, scarcely able to reconcile the searing story she had heard with the burnt-out old man lying weakly on the bed.

'That is the truth?' She questioned it involuntarily, though never really doubting it.

'It is.' He raised his head from the supporting pillows to peer at her. 'What do you think of it?'

'Why, you old rogue,' she accused him, dimples appearing in her cheeks.

He laughed, clutching her hand. 'Did I ever pretend to be anything else?'

'No, but I understand so much more now. Your strictness, the way you have reared me. I represent nearly seventeen years of endeavour, do I not?'

'Aye, but I begrudge none of it.' His grip on her hand had tightened. 'I don't know which will be hardest to leave behind—you or my money.'

Dominga's throat tightened, but she answered lightly: 'Would you have me fool enough to believe I could tip the scales against your money? I must send for the doctor immediately. Your brain must be inflamed.'

Laughter shook Wilfrid's gaunt frame. 'And you call me a rogue. I always knew the devil wreaked his vengance by saddling me with you.'

'Do not shift the blame,' she admonished him sternly. 'But my mother a gypsy! And sold to you. Papa, that was infamous!'

'She was willing enough, greedy little minx. Not much more than twenty years old, but she cared more for jewels than any man. I was the one who lusted. The middle years are dangerous for a man. 'Twas the only uncalculated thing I ever did in my life when I wed her, but it turned out right.'

'She would have been a serious embarrassment to your plans for me had she lived,' Dominga mused.

'I realised that when my passion for her had cooled and I was my own man again. I knew any offspring we might have would be dark of colouring, which was why I gave her a Spanish name to sign when we were wed.'

'But surely you could never have passed her off as Spanish?'

'Fortunately, it didn't come to that. I bought a place in Cumberland to settle her while she awaited you, and a grand time she had playing lady of the manor, but there was no taming her.'

'I cannot imagine you embroiling yourself in such a marriage,' Dominga told him frankly.

'Every man's a fool once in his life. It was her wild ways that did for her, when you were no more than a year. Storms fascinated her. She would go out and walk in the rain and, aye, dance in it like a mad woman.'

'And after one particular storm her body was recovered from a river?' Dominga questioned. 'How did she fall in?'

'I didn't push her, tempted I might have been. No, I was in London at the time. Her death was a mystery, but as an old pack-horse bridge crumbled when the river rose, it was supposed she must have been standing on it.'

'Poor woman,' Dominga murmured, but she could feel little for the mother she had never known.

'Ah, well, 'tis long over and done with but you can see, Milady, that of all my schemes you are the grandest.'

'Your efforts shall not be wasted,' Dominga vowed, as much on her own behalf as her father's. 'But the truth must never come out.'

'It won't. The web I've woven to conceal your mother's origins is so thick that nobody should ever see through it. No, I'm certain that I've contrived too long and too deep for disaster to strike you, and tell you only just in case.'

'I'm glad you did.'

'Truth is armour, though it's lies that will win your coronet. If the worst should happen, you must contrive in your turn. I've trained you for that, as well as the high position you will occupy.'

'Don't worry, Papa. Whatever happens, I'll contrive . . .'

Wilfrid looked at her indulgently. 'You're still set on Deversham?'

'I am.' Her jaw jutted slightly.

'It pleases me you have a fancy for him. I know what it's like to feel like dirt beneath an aristocrat's feet, which is why I swore my grandchildren would be born noble, but I'd like you to be happy. You think you could be happy with a man glimpsed but once?'

'I'm sure I could.' Dominga privately thought that if there were any sweetness in revenge, she could taste it to the full and relish it. That, surely, would be happiness?

She added: 'I will get Deversham, Papa?'

'With my gold to line his pockets and your cleverness, of course! Mind, if there was any justice, your face alone would make you a countess. You're as beautiful as your mother, and I never expected to see her like again.'

Dominga kissed his brow. 'Please rest now. My ambitions can wait. I've no wish to part with you yet.'

'Huh! You'll be best off without me. It's easier to gloss over a memory than the man himself.'

'Don't say so, Papa! I'd rather have you alive than any title.'

'Prettily said, but you don't mean it. Not if you're my daughter you don't.'

'Hush, or I'll pour another odious potion down your throat,' Dominga threatened him.

'Nay, Milady, tip it in the vase, the way you always do. It does me no good but it pleases your step-mother to think I've taken it. The bottle that makes this sickness bearable is in the drawer where you hid it after I last needed it. Fetch it now. I've talked myself into a thirst.'

Dominga did so. She poured some of the golden liquid into his medicine glass. He drank it down, closed his eyes and slept.

She stared down at him, wondering what other secrets were stored in that crafty brain of his. But whatever secrets there might have been were clearly not a burden upon his soul for he revealed no more. He died, as he had expected, within a few days.

He was survived no longer than two months by Harry George St John Huntsleigh, sixth Earl of Deversham, Baron of Pemberton, Banton, Raversley and Wytterby. That reckless young nobleman had breathed his last in a more spectacular but not entirely unforeseen manner. He had broken his neck while out hunting.

Dominga had heard of it, for her father had set up a

source of information that reached within the stately walls
of the Deversham stronghold. It made her fret for deliver-
ance from deep mourning and the schoolroom. Young
ladies did not enter Society until they were seventeen. Nor
did they wed until grass grew over their fathers' graves.

Dominga was impatient to secure the seventh Earl before he had a chance to break his neck also. Whether he was
the blue-eyed or the grey-eyed twin mattered little to her.

The grey-eyed one had gambled her away lightly enough,
and she had no doubt that if he had won the toss he'd have
paid her off as contemptuously as his brother. As for the
blue-eyed one . . . yes, Dominga had to admit she did have
a preference. How she would love to toss his guineas back
to him, those guineas she had stored and stared at and
plotted over these past years.

Dominga had fretted and fumed until the completion of
six months' mourning, the arrival of her seventeenth birth-
day and the new Earl's return from Europe after Waterloo,
all of which had occurred within the last week.

So here she was at last, in the City chambers of Horace
Ponting, the man her Papa had directed her to as the best
person to further her schemes.

Mr Ponting sat behind his desk, head slumped on his
chest in deep thought, as she reviewed the events which had
brought her here.

He came out of his reverie about the same time Dominga
came out of hers, and thumped his fist on the desk. 'By
George, I think we can do it,' he declared.

Dominga smiled. 'Assuredly we can. Tell me how you
propose to play your part.'

CHAPTER
THREE

MR PONTING did so, and Dominga listened carefully. Sometimes she questioned and sometimes she advised.

Grateful as she was to be endowed with her mother's looks, she knew that her survival in the frivolous though censorious world she wished to enter would depend on instincts passed down through the paternal line. Certainly she must manage better than her mother. She could scarcely manage worse . . .

At last, Mr Ponting leaned back in his chair and asked: 'You approve of my strategy, my dear?'

Since they were now fellow conspirators he felt he could afford to be a little familiar. But only a little. He was beginning to believe he was addressing the future Countess of Deversham. Some of Dominga's certainty had rubbed off on him.

'I approve,' said Dominga decisively. 'You will find me at Chersey Manor when you need me. Any expenses you incur on my behalf will naturally be added to the sum we have agreed upon.'

Mr Ponting beamed. What a delightful young lady to do business with. If only her father had been half as amiable!

Then something that had been hovering at the back of his mind, the fatal flaw he had feared in the scheme, occurred to him. The smile slipped from his face. He clapped a hand to an anguished brow as sweat broke out.

'Miss Romero-Browne! What are we about? You cannot know that the sixth Earl was killed recently. We are plotting over a corpse!'

'Nothing so grisly,' she returned equably. 'I knew.'

'But you said that your father had had this scheme in hand for some time, and he has been dead these six months. Was it not the sixth Earl you wished to marry?'

'He was one of them,' she conceded.

'I beg your pardon?' .Once more fear that she was deranged reared itself between Mr Ponting and his five hundred guineas.

'I mean that the seventh Earl will do just as well.'

'You mean it is the title that is important to you, not the man?' His rosy vision of romance blurred to the point of obscurity.

'Decidedly it is the man,' she replied. 'I could get another title without half the fuss. There are many aristocrats less particular than the Devershams.'

Mr Ponting was as much at sea as ever, but he strove to understand. 'The brothers were much alike, I take it?'

'They were twins.' Briefly, she saw again the tall, fair-haired handsomeness of them. Remembered how god-like they had seemed to her two years ago, before she had been swiftly disillusioned.

'Ah! Now I see how it is,' exclaimed Mr Ponting. 'Both dashing young men, I daresay? Not much to choose between the two of 'em?'

He foundered here, unable to equate desire with a dual target, but he struggled on with: 'They were identical, perhaps? You wish to marry one but have no irrevocable partiality to overcome? I mean, the sixth Earl popping off does not leave you inconsolable since the seventh is as alike as a pea in a pod?'

She smiled. 'You have thought your way through to the heart of the matter.'

'Good, good,' Mr Ponting mopped his brow. 'It's a relief to me that the seventh Earl will make you as happy as the sixth would have done, had he been spared. I thought—I really thought—we had encountered a dreadful stumbling block there.'

'I always contrive to avoid stumbling blocks,' she told him calmly, and in perfect truth.

Then she rose and held out a gloved hand to him. 'I must bid you good day, Mr Ponting. My step-mama will fret if I do not return to Chersey today.'

Mr Ponting took her slender hand, bowing low over it. He escorted her to the door and through the outer office. His clerks laboured on, not daring to raise their heads.

Mr Ponting felt no pity for them, nor did he think himself

a tyrant. He, too, had toiled long and unceasingly on one of those hard stools before he had risen in the world.

In the street, he said: 'You did not bring your own carriage?'

Dominga fastidiously lifted her hem away from a rotting pile of rubbish. 'No. Neither did I bring my maid, as you must have observed. Very naughty of me, but I am incognito.'

She unfurled her parasol to protect her complexion from the sun as she waited for a hackney.

'Just so.' Mr Ponting fell back on those useful words for there were none to describe precisely what he was thinking.

How such a delectable young lady believed she could travel anywhere incognito—even garbed in something less spectacular than the lavender ensemble—was quite beyond him.

Humour glowed in her eyes as she read his expression. 'In the unlikely event of anybody who is of importance observing me in the City, I shall naturally deny that I was ever here.'

'Naturally.' Mr Ponting bowed.

'So, also, will you.'

'Of course.' His bow deepened.

'And I shall never wear lavender again,' she went on reflectively.

This he could not allow. 'You must! It so becomes you.'

'And I thought that I became it. How we do delude ourselves, Mr Ponting.'

He was thrown into confusion. 'Not so. Dash it, I meant . . . that is . . . Pray allow me to send one of my clerks after a hackney. It is not right for you to be kept waiting.'

'Gibbons set off in search of one the moment we appeared on the street,' she informed him.

'Gibbons?'

'My—er—footman.' She quelled the laughter rising within her, for anybody less like a footman than Gibbons could not be imagined.

Seeing the question in Mr Ponting's eyes, she elaborated: 'My trusted footman. He accompanies me whenever I am—ah—incognito.'

'Quite so.' Again, there was nothing else Mr Ponting could think of to say.

Dominga went on musingly: 'One thing more, Mr Ponting. When you meet the Earl, observe closely the colour of his eyes. I wish most particularly to know whether they are blue or grey.'

'Of what account can that be, pray?' He wished she would cease her unexpected utterances.

'A great deal, I promise you.'

'You bewilder me. Blue or grey? What possible bearing can that have on this matter?'

'It will let me know in advance which particular enemy I have in my sights.'

'Enemy?' Mr Ponting's voice rose incredulously.

'A bad word. I will amend it. Quarry. When one is hunting, it is as well to know which prey one is after.'

'You baffle me!'

'Oh, dear, that is too bad of me.' She went on with the air of a tutor instructing a child: 'I wish to know which Earl I am to marry.'

'The seventh!' Mr Ponting spluttered. 'The sixth is dead.'

'Certainly, but which twin is the seventh?'

Mr Ponting was thunderstruck. 'Don't you know?'

'I will when you tell me whether his eyes are blue or grey,' she explained patiently.

''Pon my word! Ah, could it be that the colour of the eyes is the only difference between 'em?'

'The only difference that is immediately noticeable,' Dominga replied.

'Then you do have a preference?'

Dominga shrugged. 'The one with the grey eyes will be the easier to manage, I believe, but the one with the blue will be the more challenging. A biddable husband will suit my purposes well, though I must confess there is an imp in me which cannot resist a challenge. However, I must wait and see which it is to be.'

Mr Ponting began to splutter but he was saved the need for coherence by the arrival of a hackney carriage. As it came to a halt, the door opened. Gibbons jumped out.

'I've scoured the City for a decent hackney for you, Miss Dominga, but the first two I stopped weren't fit to put a pig in, let alone a lady dressed up finer than a Sunday dinner. This ain't much better, but let it be a lesson to you not to travel in hired hacks. If your father's toes weren't turned up already, they would be now at the thought of such a thing.'

Mr Ponting's eyes almost started out of his head at the servant's impertinence, but Dominga merely said: 'Don't scold so, Gibbons, unless it is your intention to keep me standing in the street all day.'

Thus recalled to his duties, Sam Gibbons helped his mistress into the carriage and held his peace—apart from admonishing her to keep her skirts well clear of the straw on the floor. It was his belief, he grumbled, that the carriage was full of non-paying passengers that jumped and bit.

Then he closed the door, advised her to sit tight although he was nigh on certain that the reins were in sober hands, and jumped up beside the indignant driver.

Dominga leaned through the window to say sweetly to Mr Ponting: 'Dear Gibbons was charged by my father when I was very young to keep me out of scrapes. He has yet to realise that I'm grown up and don't fall into them anymore.'

'Hmmph,' snorted the shamelessly eavesdropping Gibbons.

Dominga ignored him, waved to Mr Ponting, and was borne from his sight.

When the hackney turned the corner, Mr Ponting still stood there, loosening his modest cravat with strangely nerveless fingers.

He felt quite dazed. What an improbable young lady! If she succeeded in her schemes, she would make a most outrageous countess.

Without quite knowing why, since he had a considerable sum depending on a satisfactory outcome, Mr Ponting began to feel quite sorry for the seventh Earl of Deversham.

CHAPTER
FOUR

MR PONTING was not to know that his sympathy would have been brushed aside with contempt by Hugo St John Huntsleigh, seventh Earl of Deversham, had he but known of it. Indeed, as Hugo prepared to leave his London mansion that sunny morning, only the most addle-pated would have supposed that he stood in need of such a maudlin emotion.

Yet it was the case. Hugo's life had been radically changed by the death of his brother, and not for the better. As a younger son, and free to follow whatever calling he pleased, the role of a Hussar officer in an army at war had suited him admirably. It had cost him more than a pang to sell out, to leave the camaraderie of his fellow cavalry officers, and assume the burden of an Earldom.

And burden it undoubtedly was because of the frightful mess his twin had made of everything.

Something of this was known to Stanton, Hugo's valet, but he knew no words of consolation he might offer would be acceptable. The Earl's pride forbade it, even if he had been in an approachable mood, which was not the case this morning. Far from it.

Stanton was an old soldier and therefore nothing if not cautious. One glance at milord's set features was sufficient to make him hold his tongue. He didn't so much as cough as he settled a long and voluminous driving cape over the Earl's muscular shoulders. The cape would shield from dust his master's exquisitely tailored coat of blue superfine and, hopefully, his fawn breeches. Though civilian clothes could not compare with the magnificent Hussar's uniform that Stanton was accustomed to dressing his master in, the former soldier was not dissatisfied as he stepped back to await further commands.

His faded blue eyes, for Stanton was some ten years older than the thirty-five years he admitted to, held a hint of anxiety which was not caused by Hugo's appearance.

All was elegance there, from milord's curly-brimmed high-crowned beaver—set at a rakish angle on the fair head—to the swinging tassels of the highly-polished Hessian boots.

No, the anxiety stemmed from the closed look about his master's handsome features. It was a young face that Stanton studied, for Hugo was but four and twenty, and the valet had seen it in many moods. Yet Stanton had not seen that aristocratic countenance look so grim since it seemed those Frenchies would prevail at Waterloo. Milord should not look like this. He was about to visit a lady. His special lady.

All was well in that direction, at least. Stanton knew the Earl's passion was returned. So why the brow of thunder? Stanton's anxiety deepened, and Hugo noticed it.

He chose, however, not to enlighten his servant. Ordinarily he would have done so, for there was a closeness between them that had sprung from dangers and hardships shared, good times and bad. Hugo remained tight-lipped because this was one matter that could not be spoken of. The issue, in any case, was still uncertain.

Yet what miracle could happen between here and Wimbledon to enable him to draw back from the step he must take? Hugo had ceased to expect one but it was impossible to give up hope.

'When may we expect you back, my lord?' Stanton ventured.

'When I arrive,' Hugo snapped, and instantly regretted venting his bad temper on his servant. Yet so black was his mood that he could not bring himself to make amends. He merely swung on his heel and strode towards the door of his bedchamber.

His soldierly bearing would be with him all his life, thought Stanton, who bore the same stamp, with satisfaction. The Earl might be a credit to his valet but he was mercifully no fop. He had no patience with neck-stretching cravats nor did he load his person with diamond tie-pins, fobs, seals or walking canes. He did not even bother to carry a snuff box, that vital hallmark of any gentleman. Hugo loathed the stuff, which merely proved to the Polite

World that eccentricity was to be expected of an Earl of Deversham.

Stanton hurried forward so that he might reach the door before Hugo. It was more than he could bear to see his master looking so blue-devilled.

'Whatever it is, my lord, it can't be as bad as facing Boney's cavalry. A wall of steel they looked, if you remember, and invincible. But they weren't, and you came out of that with no more than a scratch,' Stanton said earnestly.

'What the devil has that to do with anything?' Hugo demanded.

'Only that whatever is amiss this day, it cannot be worse than *that* day.'

'Deuced lot you know about it,' Hugo growled. Then, seeing that Stanton's eyes did not waver and fall before his, his expression softened slightly.

'I swear you'll be facing something worse than French cavalry if you don't let me pass,' he added softly.

'Now, now, sir,' Stanton cautioned, glad that he had almost wrung a smile from the Earl. He turned the handle, opened the door and stepped aside.

He dared to add: 'Don't be forgetting that if Boney could be beat, then so could any trouble that's casting a damper on your spirits right now. Think on that, my lord. It will cut your problems down to size, just as if they were enemy cavalry.'

'Do not tempt me to tell you what you can do with your homespun philosophy,' Hugo advised, striding out into the wide passage.

'Yes, sir,' said Stanton obediently, and waited.

Hugo paused briefly. 'You may expect me home for luncheon.'

'Yes, sir.' Stanton accepted this peace-offering with satisfaction, retreated into milord's bedchamber and closed the door.

As he tended the Earl's discarded riding clothes, for Hugo had ridden far and hard before breakfast, Stanton felt deeply affected by his master's despondency.

He had thought it very hard when Lord Hugo had had to leave the Regiment to assume the Earldom because his brother had been inconsiderate enough to break his neck.

There had been a delay of several weeks, to see Boney beaten, but the step had finally had to be taken. Stanton had been unable to envisage anything worse than that, but it seemed he had been wrong. His master had inherited a parcel of debts along with his fine title, and Stanton could only hope that the Earl's lady would cheer him up.

French she was, but if she could bring back the gleam to milord's eyes and the laugh to his lips, then Stanton thought he might at last forgive her for that. She was not a Republican, after all. And she had the advantage of being born in this country since her parents, the Comte and Comtesse de Lafayeure, had fled the dreadful revolution years before.

Nothing like the upheaval across the Channel had happened in England for donkey's years, so Stanton felt quite justified in his contempt for the French goings-on. He was for the established order, and always would be. But, even more, he was for his master.

If the French lady could make milord happy, then Stanton was prepared to accept her instead of a proper English lady. He would even practise twisting his sensible English tongue around her outlandish name . . .

Oblivious to the ramblings of his valet's mind, Hugo ran down the curved marble staircase of Deversham House. The frown was back on his face as he crossed the great marble hall, which was a tribute to some ancestor's interest in Roman architecture.

The footman who spent his days on guard at the massive front door, opened it so smartly that Hugo was able to pass through without a pause. A curt nod was all he got for his alacrity, so at least one other servant knew that his master was in a black mood.

Hugo crossed the pavement to his waiting phaeton. Damn you, Harry, he thought. How like you to raise the devil and leave me to pay his bill.

That had always been the case, but Hugo had not minded. Though he was the younger of the twins, he had early shown himself in every way to be the more capable of the two. This time, however, he minded very much. On his shoulders had fallen the burden of the Deversham debts. He was not the man to wilt under any responsibility, but it was with something like despair that he sprang up into the phaeton.

He was going to lose Désirée.

He could stand all the rest, but that he could not bear. He loved her. He loved her desperately. His jaw tightened. The fine square, basking in the summer sun, held no charm for him. He took up the reins and nodded grimly to his groom.

Parsons, splendidly attired in the blue and silver of the Deversham livery, released the horses' heads and leapt smartly up into the phaeton. Settling his cockaded hat more firmly on his head, he also observed that all was not well with the Earl.

Parsons had been raised at Deversham Hall in Hampshire, the son of an under-gardener. He had gone into the Army with Lord Hugo as his groom, since he had more feeling for mettlesome thoroughbreds than ever he would for vegetables and flowers.

And like Stanton—who had been acquired as a servant in Spain on the death through pneumonia of Hugo's civilian valet—he had left the Army with his master. Having been reared in proper awe of the Huntsleighs, a circumstance not shared by Stanton, Parsons did not presume to talk milord into a more sanguine frame of mind.

Which was just as well. Hugo would not have appreciated it. For some time his mind was blessedly absorbed with the need to manoeuvre the phaeton through the crush of drays, wagons, hand-carts, hacks and private vehicles which crammed the London streets.

As soon as he was in the open country, however, and able to give the matched greys their heads, his mind reverted to his troubles. Curse his twin for his feckless ways! The hunting accident might have solved all Harry's problems, but it had also robbed Hugo of his promised bride.

A sudden vision of Désirée in another man's arms made Hugo's face twist with pain. She belonged in *his* arms. How would she take the news he was bringing her? Hugo felt an urge to turn the phaeton round, to delay their meeting for one more day of hope. But what hope could there be?

Unlike his brother, it was not in Hugo's nature to shirk what must be done, but his resolution almost wavered at

that moment. He slowed the horses, deliberated, then
urged them on. He felt as if he was driving to his own doom.

Such happiness he and Désirée had known! And so
briefly . . .

What a devil's coil it was and no way out, save the one he
was about to take. If she argued with him, pleaded, Hugo
knew he would be lost. He would sweep her into his arms
and forget all the rest. He would stay true to his love. But,
by doing so, he would be playing the traitor to his name and
all it meant. He could not save the Deversham estates and
have Désirée.

Désirée was what he wanted. Deversham was his duty.
Was ever a man faced with such a dilemma?

Désirée or Deversham . . . the choice revolved in his
brain as it had through these past days, until it had seemed
that madness itself would loom to end his pain.

This morning, after another restless night, Hugo had
resolved that Deversham must come first. He would do his
duty. Unless Désirée pleaded . . .

He hoped she wouldn't and prayed that she would. If he
could have placed his hands around Harry's neck right
then, he would have broken it himself.

For Hugo knew that Désirée loved him. The anguish of
those weeks in Brussels, when he had not known, was
nothing to the anguish he felt now at having to relinquish
her. Hugo's heart constricted. Again he felt like committing murder. But whose, since Harry was beyond him, and
to what effect, he did not know. Certainly no savagery
could free him from the yoke Harry had shackled him with.
Only Désirée crushed against his chest could ease this
pent-up emotion. Désirée . . . no woman had ever been
more aptly named.

Hugo remembered how soft and yielding her body had
been against his, how eager her lips, how fervent her
embraces.

She had teased him and provoked and prevaricated. But
at the Duchess of Richmond's ball on the eve of Waterloo,
she had changed in an instant.

When the Allied officers had been ordered to rejoin their
regiments because Napoleon had stolen a march on them,
Désirée had flung herself into Hugo's arms and clung to

him. She had been no cool and accomplished Society flirt then. Just a girl frantic at the thought of the man she loved going off to battle.

She had cast aside all worldly consideration with the very act of throwing herself into his arms. She loved her English milord, even though he had not the great fortune she had set herself to marry, and had incoherently told him so.

Just as incoherently, Hugo had kissed her. He had meant to soothe her fears and ease his own desire but he had only succeeded in inflaming them both. They had seemed moulded together, her silken-clad body crushed against his splendid Hussar dress uniform, as they had tried to live a whole lifetime of love in moments. While officers departed and civilians danced on, the curtained alcove which concealed them seemed a world apart as they had pledged their troth.

But now the world had intruded with a vengeance. The battle was over. Hugo had returned to London to discover the appalling extent of his brother's debts. His own debts now.

The competence Hugo had inherited from his mother had been sufficient to purchase his commission and support him in comfort and ease. It would also have supported Désirée, since she had vowed herself willing to forgo the flamboyant lifestyle she had formerly craved. Now that income was just a drop in the ocean against the commitments Hugo had inherited. Everything was mortgaged up to the hilt. No tradesman had been paid for years. If Harry had been anything less than the Earl of Deversham he would have been clapped in the Fleet long ago, but his creditors were crafty. They could wait.

There were thousands of Deversham acres scattered about the country, over several estates. The sale of them, even after the mortgages had been redeemed, would yield a good return. The creditors knew they would eventually get their money, even if the seventh Earl was not left with a shirt to his back.

Hugo cared little for his shirt but he did care about his acres. He was not, as yet, sure how many of the secondary estates he could salvage from the débâcle but he was determined that his principal seat should be saved. Deversham Hall would not, could not, go under the hammer. His mind recoiled from that as violently as it recoiled from the thought of life without Désirée. Yet one or the other must go, for no miracle had happened thus far on the way to Wimbledon.

Désirée had been one of the aristocrats who had flocked to Brussels to wine and dine in the weeks before the battle, and afterwards she had returned home with her mother.

Hugo had stayed on in Belgium for a while, completing his duties in the aftermath of Waterloo. His return to London a few days ago had been eager, his pressing need to see Désirée—but his agent and steward had got to him first. The papers they had placed before him had revealed the enormity and imminence of the disaster about to engulf the Deversham holdings. The light had died from Hugo's eyes, the hope from his heart.

He understood rapidly that he had not returned, as he had imagined, to claim his lady, but to the death of all his dreams of her . . .

The Earl reached his destination sooner than he wanted to, yet he knew no amount of time could fully prepare him for the interview that must now take place. He surveyed with brooding eyes the house that sheltered his love. It was respectable but no mansion. It had been built less than thirty years before on solid rather than inspired lines.

The Comtesse de Lafayeure hated it. She had endured nobly enough her exile from her native land while the Comte had been alive, for they had lived in a stylish house in the best quarter of London. The Comte's death some years previously—he had ruined his liver by drinking excessive amounts of brandy to console himself for the loss of his château in the Loire valley—had brought this comfortable existence to an end.

The Comtesse, in dire financial straits, had been forced to retreat with her children to unfashionable Wimbledon and this ugly house. Not a day passed but she bewailed their cramped conditions, since the house boasted no more than eight bedrooms. It was, for a lady such as herself, unendurable. But she had endured. By quietly disposing of her jewels when occasion demanded it, she had lived for the day when she could regain the gracious living Napoleon's mad schemes had deprived her of.

She had suffered two disappointments already.

Her eldest daughter had eloped with an officer of no more than a line regiment, and was living so frugally that she now regretted her impetuous act as bitterly as her mother.

The Comtesse's second daughter had renounced all ambition and disappeared behind the thick walls of a convent. The Comtesse had taken to her bed for upwards of a month. When she finally emerged from her bedchamber she announced that she washed her hands of her second daughter as thoroughly as that daughter had washed her hands of the world, and had concentrated on the third.

With Désirée—the most beautiful and promising of all the girls—the Comtesse found herself facing the yawning pit of another disappointment. Well, it must not happen.

There was a fourth daughter yet to be launched. There was also a son, the youngest of the brood, who was causing her a great deal of expense over the matter of his education. When he entered Society, he would cost her more. And the Comtesse had no more jewels to sell. She had hazarded all on Désirée, hoping that with a brilliant match all would come right for the de Lafayeures.

For the first months of Désirée's entrance into Society, the Comtesse had no cause to regret the disposal of her diamonds, for her daughter had taken the town by storm.

All the gentlemen were at Désirée's feet, and the Comtesse had carefully weeded out the improvident ones. Of those who remained, and there had been many, the Comtesse declared magnanimously that Désirée might have her pick.

Was ever a girl so lucky? The Comtesse did not think so, and neither did her daughter. Désirée enjoyed her success enormously, but she did not let it go to her head.

Within that region ticked much of her mother's calculating brain. Désirée was on the point of putting her richest suitor out of his misery when her beautiful eyes had alighted on Hugo Huntsleigh.

She thought it grossly unfair that fate should have introduced her to such a man because, although by birth he was eminently suitable, by fortune he was not.

Désirée, like her mother, dreamed of riches. She had not known until now what it was like to dream of a man. She had been brought up most sensibly to regard men as a means to an end, not as an end in themselves. But Lord Hugo could not be repulsed as easily as her other unsuitable admirers. Something about him touched her senses. He was so handsome and noble, this dashing Hussar. He had captivated her against her will.

They made such a handsome couple, too—a pity it was such an impossible one. This Désirée had decided without her mother's urgings until that fatal ball in Brussels had undone her. In that fraught and dynamic atmosphere, when the Allied officers had rushed off to an unknown fate, Désirée had known a heady moment of madness.

She had declared her love for Hugo, terrified that he might be killed. Now, after much calm reflection in a totally different atmosphere, she was forced to conclude that perhaps it would have been better for her had Hugo not survived the carnage of Waterloo.

These thoughts could not help but lower her spirits, but they did not dim her beauty as her mother came to announce that the Earl had arrived.

The Comtesse surveyed her daughter narrowly. 'I feel for you, *ma petite*, but I trust to your good sense. You must not throw away the world for love. Marry Marsham. He may have no title, but his lineage is impeccable and his fortune second to none.'

When Désirée did not answer, the Comtesse went on: 'Marsham will shower you with jewels. He adores you, *chérie*, and pampering you will be his delight. I know you well, and nothing less than having your every whim granted will make you happy. Later, you may satisfy your passion for Deversham.'

'What if that passion cannot be satisfied, Mama, but lasts forever?'

'Pouf!' The Comtesse snapped her fingers. 'There is no such passion.'

She laughed roguishly, looking almost as entrancing as her daughter in that moment. 'There are only two abiding things in life—wealth and position. Love comes and goes. One takes it where one finds it, if it is convenient. Look at your eldest sister if you doubt me. What has she got from her grand passion? Dingy rooms in Kensington, of all places, and nothing to cheer her but might-have-beens.'

'But Hugo isn't an officer of a line regiment,' Désirée objected. 'Indeed, he is now an Earl.'

'He is not as rich as Marsham. He reaps the harvest of debts sown by his ancestors. I have enquired most particularly into that and Deversham is—is *finis!*'

Désirée studied her reflection in the mirror. Her alabaster complexion was slightly flushed at the prospect of meeting Hugo again, and her breathing was not quite as even as she would have liked. Nevertheless, she looked composed as she went downstairs to greet the only man who had ever touched her heart. Like Hugo, she was ready to do her duty.

In the salon into which he had been shown, Hugo stood by the window looking out into the grounds. They were not extensive but presented a pleasant aspect, had Hugo been in an appreciative mood. Unlike the house, the unlovely proportions of which she could do nothing about, the Comtesse had been able to have the gardens landscaped to suit her fastidious taste. But like everything else on this fateful morning, they found little favour in Hugo's brooding eyes, and he turned slowly as the door opened.

Désirée stood there, framed for a moment in the doorway. Tense though this moment of their reunion was, she posed instinctively for her lover's appreciation.

Hugo's heart lurched. She was so very lovely. Fragile as a delicate piece of Dresden china, and just as perfect.

Désirée was not tall but she was very slender. Her pale complexion, pampered with Olympian Dew and bathed with citron water if freckles threatened—for the Comtesse had spared no expense in the matter of her daughter's beauty—had indeed the quality of fine china.

Her blue eyes were large and fringed with dark lashes. Her little nose was straight, and so were her white teeth. Her rosebud lips were not full enough to suggest sensuality but they were soft enough to tempt.

Her golden hair curled naturally. It was artfully arranged in bunches of ringlets over her dainty ears, from which trembled tiny pearls.

She was a veritable golden girl. The yellow gown she wore was made of muslin which, on her, seemed more like gossamer. The gown exposed something of her shoulders and all of her graceful neck. It would have taken a man of iron to have resisted her and this, when it came to beautiful ladies, Hugo most definitely was not.

'Désirée . . .' He crossed the room in swift strides to clasp her hands and kiss them ardently.

From there he was just a hair's breadth away from sweeping her into his arms but Désirée, anticipating him, stepped back slightly. The movement recalled Hugo to sanity and his mission. He let go of her hands and widened the space between them.

Still he was vulnerable to her attraction, still he wished to crush her against him as he had at the Duchess's ball. He had been through such hell since then that it seemed a lifetime ago. But he could not wish that it had never happened. He must hold firm to his memories now, cherish them, since he could no longer cherish Désirée. He turned from her and strode back to the window.

Désirée was relieved. He was not going to sweep her off her feet, then. He must have become as aware as she that they could not marry. That meant the rumours circulating about the extent of the Deversham debts was true.

She could not marry a pauper, albeit a noble one. If her circumstances had been different, if she had had sufficient money to afford such a handsome bridegroom, then perhaps she would have allowed her heart to rule her head. She had done so once, in Brussels, but her mother was right. Passion could only be indulged in when one could afford it. Love matches were for the lower orders. Her class made prudent marriages.

'Hugo?' she said tentatively as the silence between them lengthened.

He could not look at her. Dared not.

'I have nothing but debts to support my title, Désirée. I don't expect you to share my life, since that would mean you would have to share them also.'

She nodded. 'I had heard. I hoped it was not true, or exaggerated.'

'One could not exaggerate the dissipation of the last

three Earls,' Hugo replied bitterly. 'I am so far in dun territory I cannot see my way clear.'

Désirée said what he could not voice himself: 'You must marry an heiress.'

He did not answer. She crossed the room and stood by his shoulder, a sudden tremor of nostalgia reminding her how once his strength had thrilled her.

He kept his gaze fixed on the garden. 'I love you, Désirée. I do not know how to let you go.'

She touched his arm, almost overwhelmed by the urge to caress him. For a moment she felt a bitterness as deep as his, but for a different reason. It was so unfair that a man could take his pleasures where he found them but a woman could not!

'I also must marry a fortune,' she told him.

He swung towards her, saying fiercely: 'What a damnable business it is! But, Désirée, you knew I was not rich when you agreed to marry me.'

'Ah, but that was in Brussels before Waterloo, when everybody was a little mad.'

'You call it madness now? We called it love at the time.'

'Everything was so different,' Désirée replied matter-of-factly. 'I did not know the extent of the debts you had inherited then, any more than you did. We allowed ourselves to feel too much and think too little.'

Hugo was silent, so she went on: 'I must marry a rich man. I have no dowry, nor precious little else.'

Hugo was arrested. 'Surely things cannot be as bad as that? Your mother launched you into Society in fine style.'

'Yes, and sold the last of her diamonds to do so. Those were fakes she wore in Brussels, Hugo. Our last asset has gone, and there is still my sister to make her début—and my brother is expensive.'

Hugo whistled. 'I did not know it was as bad as that.'

'If I do not marry a fortune our situation will be worse than your own. We do not have your name with which to obtain credit. Money-lenders are weary of impoverished French émigrés. You will discover for yourself that a distinguished name means nothing when there is no substance behind it if, heaven forbid, you are forced to sell your lands.'

Hugo clasped her hand where it rested on his sleeve. 'I would be a worse rogue than my brother if I asked you to forget all else and chance your luck with me. And yet, I feel the urge to do so, Désirée.'

She withdrew her hand. They were on dangerous ground. 'You must not abandon your responsibilities for love, Hugo.'

'Must I not?' He looked down at her, the reckless smile that had been her undoing once before upon his lips.

She felt her blood stir, but her voice when she replied was firm. 'No, you must not. And neither must I.'

'So be it.' His voice was harsh. His smile had gone.

Désirée raised her fine eyes to his and murmured: 'Perhaps there will come another time for us, Hugo.'

'What? Am I to outlive my miserable heiress and you your rich husband? What comfort is there in that? Are we to love again in our dotage?'

Désirée, who could not think of age without a shudder, replied: 'There will be a time for us long before then.'

His eyebrows drew together. 'You would cuckold your husband?'

'We are worldly people. I do not see that we must renounce each other for ever. If it gives you any comfort, I shall not love my husband.'

'It gives me no comfort at all,' Hugo retorted.

'No? Then I tell you straightly, Hugo, that it would be much comfort to me if you did not love your wife.'

'Consider yourself comforted. I could never love any woman save yourself, Désirée.'

She sighed, satisfied. 'Then there *will* be another time for us.' After a pause she asked: 'Do you have a particular heiress in mind, Hugo?'

'No.' He was watching her with brooding eyes.

'There is Isabelle Yerberry.' Désirée's casual tone conveyed none of her anxiety to implant this name upon his mind. Isabelle was too plain ever to interest Hugo, and too poor-spirited to challenge her husband's allegiance to another woman.

'Spare me,' he begged. 'She would bore me to tears within a week.'

'She is amiable enough,' Désirée pointed out.

'Is that what I am reduced to? To feel gratitude because a woman is amiable?'

'You could do worse. She is young enough to mould, and she inherits her mother's money as well as her father's. You must be practical.'

'Curse all that is practical.' Hugo turned purposefully towards her.

Désirée retreated hastily until there was a table between them. 'Hugo,' she said sharply. 'This gets us nowhere. You must go now.'

'Where to?' he flung at her. 'The devil?'

'Not you,' she answered softly. 'You are not your brother. You will come through this with Deversham intact. And do not think your heart is broken. How could it be, when I freely admit I love you still?'

'Désirée, you torment me!' he exclaimed.

She was not displeased at that, and said calmly: 'It must be duty first, for both of us. When that is done, there will still be our love.'

When he was silent, she added jealously: 'Unless, after all, you think to love your wife?'

'Never! Have I not promised you that?'

'Then I am content. Go now, Hugo, for I think perhaps you had the right of it when you mentioned torment. Being alone together can cause us nothing else. I pray we will not meet again until you are a married man and I a married lady. All will be different then, and we will find a way to ease our suffering.'

She held out her hand to him imperiously. He ignored it. He swept her into his arms and kissed her with a desperate ruthlessness that left her shaken and trembling.

Then he was gone.

The Earl was halfway back to London before his chaotic thoughts sorted themselves into some semblance of coherence.

So, it was done.

What had Désirée called the heiress, Isabelle Yerberry? Amiable? It was to be hoped she was, Hugo thought grimly, for if he found that he did not dislike her too much, she would shortly be saddled with the wretchedest of husbands.

He could not recollect her very well, conjuring up only a vague image of a shrinking female who lacked inches in height and had a surplus of them everywhere else. But Désirée was shrewd, and had no doubt named Isabelle with good reason. The heiress was too insipid to have tantrums if he was not for ever dancing attendance upon her. She was of his world and would understand well the terms of a marriage between them. Isabelle it would be, then. And to think that a man was supposed to be master of his own fate!

Hugo laughed harshly. His groom jumped, disliking the sound of it. It seemed the Earl was in no better temper after seeing his lady love than he had been before. Parsons was relieved when Deversham House was reached and he was free to escape to the stables.

Hugo entered the house and was almost across the spacious hall when his butler appeared.

Jamieson, whose emaciated frame belied the good living he enjoyed, did not appear to hurry but he managed to intercept his master before Hugo had gained the stairs.

The Earl frowned down on him and warned: 'Only a fool would get in my way this day.'

'Just so, my lord, but there is a person wishing to see you.'

'A person?' thundered Hugo. 'What person?'

'A Mr Horace Ponting from the City, my lord.'

'Have you taken leave of your senses, Jamieson? Am I to be dunned in my own house?'

The butler looked reproachfully at him. 'As if I would allow such a thing to happen. No, my lord, I bring Mr Ponting to your attention because he claims to have come upon a matter that is to your advantage.'

'That's novel, I grant you, but I don't wish to see him. Send him to the devil, with my compliments.'

'My lord . . .' Jamieson persisted.

'And you with him, if you don't go away.'

'Very well, my lord.' Jamieson stepped aside and with stately tread made for the green room, where he had left Mr Ponting waiting in some trepidation.

Jamieson thought he had earned the five guineas now

resting in his pocket. He had been right to raise the price from the one guinea he had been offered to bring Mr Ponting to the Earl's notice.

With the Earl in such a mood, indeed, Jamieson was not at all sure that he had upped the offer enough.

He opened the door to the green room and proceeded to send Mr Ponting, if not to the devil as his lordship commanded, then at least about his business.

CHAPTER
FIVE

Hugo's mood did not lighten during the day. He scarcely tasted the luncheon served to him by a cautious and correct Jamieson.

The carving knife never touched the various cold meats. The boiled tongue, which his lordship could generally be relied upon to do full justice to, was pushed aside. The goose-and-turkey pie was cut, toyed with and discarded. The fruit was ignored.

Word of this passed swiftly through the household. From the butler down to the lowliest of kitchen maids, Hugo's lack of appetite was thought to be a very bad sign. Indeed, coupled with the news gleaned from Parsons that his lordship had left the home of Mademoiselle Lafayeure in a mood more melancholy than he had arrived, it was thought to be nothing less than ominous.

Had his lordship decided that all was ruined beyond recovery?

The servants worried and fretted, for many of them came from families which had served the Earl's for generations. There had been a Jamieson, for example, on the staff rolls in King James the First's time. The Parsons had tended the gardens at Deversham Hall for almost as long, and the Leggetts had provided clerks and housekeepers since the Restoration. The present steward was a Leggett. The family histories of these servants, and many others, had become so closely bound up with the history of the noble family they served that it was impossible to separate them.

Hugo was well aware of this, and regarded the welfare of his dependants as basic a responsibility as the preservation of his lands. For the modern thinkers of the day, inspired by the republicans across the Channel, this master-servant relationship seemed positively feudal. And so it was, but neither Hugo nor his staff could look upon its breakdown as anything but catastrophic. For if the House of Deversham foundered, it would be the ruin of not one family but many.

What would the future generations of Jamiesons, Parsons and Leggetts do if there was no Earl to serve? Go into the factories and mills like other, less-favoured families? The servants couldn't bear to think about it and so they looked to Hugo to haul them off the rocks to safety.

Those closest to him strove to interpret every expression that crossed his face and relayed their information to those whose jobs never brought them into actual contact with the nobleman who paid their yearly stipends. This was why Hugo's failure to eat his luncheon inflicted gloom on even the most optimistic of his retainers.

It was noted that he retired to the library when he rose from the table, and word was passed by Jamieson that his lordship was on no account to be disturbed. Was this a good sign or bad?

There was no fear that the Earl would blow his brains out, a suspicion which would have prostrated the servants had Harry ever done anything so extraordinary as closeting himself up with a calamitous pile of bills. But then, Harry would have thought it eccentric to the point of lunacy to bother his head about creditors. Why should he, when he employed an agent for that purpose?

Whenever that hard-pressed gentleman had dared to take Harry to task over his reckless gaming away of borrowed money, he merely bade him to be a good fellow and not bother him with trifles.

That was Harry. Popular as he had been with his servants, once they had recovered from the shock of his passing, they could not but feel grateful that the reins were now in Hugo's hands.

Hugo was shrewd, capable and dependable. The servants who had watched him grow up knew that as certainly as they had known that Harry would not live long enough for the gout to get him.

Hugo had only once let them down, and that was by following his brother into the world and thus not becoming the immediate heir. Which was quite extraordinary when one came to think of it, for Hugo had been first in everything ever since. First to set his pony at a gate, first to defy his father, first to tumble a chambermaid . . .

Oh, yes, Hugo had cut as much of a dash as Harry but, having had his fun, he had always been ready to stand the buff. He had not run, nor shifted responsibility. One loved Harry, but one trusted Hugo.

But Hugo, isolated in the library, felt very little love right then for his brother. More than once, however, he wished he had his sanguine temperament.

Then he would be able to sweep aside all these damnable papers and go to one of his clubs . . . hell-bent on pleasure.

Grief, why was he not like Harry? It must be infinitely less painful to break one's neck than one's heart. Hugo resolutely recalled his wandering mind and continued to plough through the papers which his agent had sorted into piles according to priority.

At four o'clock he rang for tea. When the tray was brought in, he served himself and drank it at his desk. Word passed through the household that his lordship had partaken of a Christian beverage. He had not called for brandy. Praise be.

Hugo worked on. At seven o'clock, Jamieson knocked on the door and was given permission to enter.

The butler advanced to the desk, his deferential manner belied by the determined glint in his eye.

Did milord require candles?

No, milord did not. Any fool could see that the long summer evening provided light enough.

The butler begged pardon but lingered, for there was the matter of dinner to be considered.

One of the Deversham oddities was totally ignoring the vogue for French cooks and allowing an Englishwoman to preside over the kitchens.

Mrs Barrows was a direct descendant of a scullery maid named Lucy Howerd, who had risen to prominence in the Deversham kitchens towards the end of the reign of Good Queen Bess.

Mrs Barrows was turned sixty now, but she had a daughter waiting to step into her shoes, a fact much appreciated by the kitchen staff because all of Lucy Howerd's female descendants combined great culinary skill with a remarkable lack of temperament.

So it was that the Earl's scarcely-touched luncheon had been received back by Mrs Barrows without fuss. She was now preparing dinner for eight, not knowing whether or not his lordship would taste a morsel of it. She made no complaint, but since the servants did not eat until after the Earl, Jamieson had been beseeched on all sides to discover when—and if—this much-awaited event would take place.

And so Jamieson stood like a graven image beside the desk until such time as the Earl would deign to notice him again.

After several minutes, Hugo raised his head. 'Have you taken root, Jamieson?'

'No, my lord.'

'Then be a good fellow and go away.'

'Yes, my lord,' Jamieson replied, not budging an inch.

The Earl stared at him thoughtfully. 'Very well, what is it?'

'Dinner, my lord,' Jamieson said, grateful for the opening. 'Mrs Barrows is wishing to know whether it may be served at eight as usual.'

'Certainly it may.' Hugo turned back to his work.

Knowing full well how long it took a gentleman to dress for dinner, Jamieson persisted: 'It is past seven now.'

'Is it, by god?' Hugo glanced at the elaborate grandfather clock on the far side of the room and saw that it was in fact several minutes past the hour.

Where had the afternoon gone? His business was by no means finished. The papers awaiting his attention seemed to have scarcely diminished.

The weariness on his face was so apparent that Jamieson took the liberty an old retainer might occasionally indulge in, and told his lordship a home truth or two.

'Enough is enough, Master Hugo,' he said sternly. 'A change of raiment and a good dinner is what you need now. Those papers can wait until tomorrow, when you'll be fresh to tackle them again.'

Amusement gleamed in the Earl's eyes. 'Master Hugo, is it? If I'm being reduced to nursery rank I'd best take care I don't get my breeches dusted as well.'

Jamieson's gaunt face resembled the compressing of a lemon as he smiled. 'Now, now, it's many a long year since I dusted your breeches for you,' he replied.

'The memory, however, lingers on.' Hugo stood up and
stretched. He felt bone-weary. 'It's as well I learned when I
did the harshest rule of the household—the butler must
always be obeyed!'

Jamieson could not deny the truth of this, but he was
heartened by Hugo's smile as he left the library. He
watched the Earl bound up the stairs to his bed-chamber
and thought that, for a moment there, Hugo had seemed
rather like his old self.

What a pair of scamps he and Harry had been when they
were growing up. Jamieson sighed briefly for bygone happy
days and made his stately way to the kitchen. He thought he
might safely report that his lordship's mood was on the
mend.

Jamieson was not entirely right. What had come to the
Earl during those tedious hours in the library was not an
uplifting of spirits so much as an acceptance of his fate. He
was resigned.

His last lingering hopes that he might yet possess Désirée
as his bride had been extinguished with the thorough
perusal of those papers. It was not to be. Could never be.
He could hope for no more than possessing her, at some
time in the future, as his mistress. It was not what he
wanted, but what he would have to settle for. Meanwhile,
he would pursue Isabelle Yerberry. He had no time for a
gentle and leisurely wooing and shuddered to think what
the nuptial couch would be like.

Could a man make a bride a wife without kissing her? Or
must he delude himself into believing the lips he did not
wish to touch were Désirée's, which he could not leave
alone? Did he, Hugo Huntsleigh, have to stoop to such
deceit? Yes he did, he told himself, clenching his jaw. He
would have to remind himself of Désirée's dictum: duty
first, pleasure second.

'What invitations have we for this evening?' Hugo asked
Stanton as he strode into his bed-chamber.

Stanton fetched a silver tray and Hugo sorted through
the cards which reposed upon it.

London in July was thin of company, the fashionable
having retreated to Brighton, hence the pleasures offered

for the evening's entertainment were not impressive.

However, Hugo knew the Yerberrys were still in Town.

When Désirée had mentioned Isabelle, Hugo had remembered seeing the Yerberry carriage in Hyde Park yesterday afternoon.

What had he afforded Mrs Yerberry and her insipid daughter? A cursory nod in passing. Well, he would have to do better than that.

Hugo found the card he was seeking. It was an invitation to a soirée Mrs Yerberry was giving that evening. There would be music, cards and dancing. It would be deadly dull. None of his friends would be there, since high-living young bloods would not be seen dead at such a dreary event. Only those gentlemen hanging out for a rich bride could be counted on to attend. His appearance among them would be as good as a declaration of intent, Hugo thought gloomily.

They would be laying odds in the clubs tomorrow on when the wedding would take place. Mrs Yerberry would be cock-a-hoop, Miss Yerberry gratified—or so Hugo hoped—while he himself would feel as if he had paid the first instalment of the devil's due.

The Earl of Deversham, a gazetted fortune-hunter! A pain twisted in Hugo's chest. This time it was more than just a craving for Désirée. It was his pride suffering. That he should be reduced to this . . .

'My lord?' Stanton prompted. It was his duty to dress his master for dinner but, since he knew nothing of Hugo's plans for the evening, he had been unable to set out suitable clothes.

Hugo handed him the card. 'I shall be attending this affair.'

Stanton glanced at the card, stifled his surprise, and said impassively: 'The blue coat or the green, sir? Or there is the mustard—'

'Mustard!' Hugo exclaimed. 'I never had a mustard coat.'

'The Stultz coat,' Stanton prompted him.

'Dammit, man, Weston is my tailor.'

'Nevertheless, my lord, there is the mustard coat from Stultz. You bespoke it last year when you were in Town on leave . . . on the day you spent with your brother.'

'Oh, that explains it. I must have been a trifle disguised.'

Stanton did not argue with this massive understatement, merely adding: 'You wish me to dispose of the coat, my lord?'

'If you had any sense, you would have done so when it was delivered.'

Stanton was pleased with having picked the right time to remind Hugo of the offensive coat. Disposing of Hugo's discarded garments was one of the perks of his profession, and the valet's current ladybird was proving rather expensive.

'The blue coat then, my lord?' he suggested.

Hugo had had enough. 'I don't give a straw what colour it is, just move yourself. I want a drink before dinner.'

Stanton did move himself. He dressed his master faster than most valets would have deemed possible.

His expression gave nothing away, but his mind was seething with speculation. The Earl was visiting the Yerberrys this evening . . . So the mademoiselle was out of the running in the countess stakes, and the heiress was in.

Throughout all the great houses in the land there was an information network in operation among the servants. So Stanton knew that Mrs Yerberry, who had been hanging out grimly for a duke for her daughter, was now ready to grab an earl after four unsuccessful seasons of endeavour.

Hugo was well aware of what was running through his valet's mind. Stanton knew the Yerberrys did not form part of Hugo's usual set and he would jump to the only possible conclusion.

Hugo preserved his silence until his neckcloth was safely tied, then met his valet's eyes. 'Well, Stanton?' he asked. 'Do I have your approval?'

Stanton did not pretend to misunderstand. He knew it was not an opinion of the cravat his lordship was seeking.

'I hear Miss Yerberry is very well bred, sir, and—'

'Extremely well heeled?' supplied the Earl cynically.

'That is correct. She is also extremely dull, by all accounts.'

'A man doesn't look for liveliness in his wife,' Stanton suggested quietly.

'Does he not?' Hugo questioned mockingly.

'No, my lord. His mistresses supply that.'

Hugo's lips twitched into a smile. 'What the devil do you know about the matter? You've never had a wife.'

'No, my lord, and now you know why.'

Hugo laughed, then said: 'Be thankful you haven't an earldom to support.'

'I am, seeing as how I wasn't bred to it.' Stanton was thawing into his real self under the mellowness of his master's mood. 'It's different for you.'

'Is it?' Hugo asked reflectively. 'I wonder . . .'

'There's no sense in wondering. Things are as they are, and you're an earl now, like it or not. And if I might make so bold, sir, the sooner you get used to it the better. Your temper these past days has had everybody on the hop. I'm glad to see you're coming out of it at last.'

Hugo, having already endured one homily from his butler, said dangerously: 'Are you so sure of that, Stanton?'

'Yes, or you wouldn't be talking to me like—like you always used to when we were in the Regiment. Like I was human, sir.'

Hugo stared at him. 'Dammit, do you presume to put me in my place?'

Stanton grinned at him. 'You never said, when you took me on, as how I'd have to tell you lies.'

'What an appalling oversight. I wonder why I did take you on?'

'You were hard-pressed, if you remember, with your man dying from pneumonia so sudden-like, and me having some experience as a batman. Not that I could see you getting on with any toffee-nosed London valet as would have a fit every time you got a speck of dust on your boots. You ain't one to be fussed, and a valet having vapours is what you could not stand.'

Hugo murmured: 'A valet with no sensibility might be reckoned worse than one with too much.'

Stanton snorted, a derisive sound which amused rather than offended the Earl. He walked over to the long-mirror, which Stanton tilted to the right angle, and studied his appearance.

His white cravat was neat rather than spectacular and the

starched points of his collar aspired to no more than modest height. Being no dandy, the Earl liked to move his head without having to move his shoulders as well. His coat of dark blue superfine looked well with his superbly-cut fawn breeches. He wore no jewels on his long fingers. The crested ring worn by all Deversham earls was being enlarged, Hugo's fingers being thicker than Harry's.

He slipped the fob watch Stanton handed him into his waistcoat pocket and glanced briefly at his crisply waving fair hair, which was brushed out of his way rather than for effect, and was too short to be strictly fashionable. Hugo looked very much the man. His coat needed no buckram wadding to make it set well on his shoulders. His legs were sufficiently muscled to show his breeches to advantage, yet he studied his appearance with indifferent eyes.

It mattered little. He had no assignation with Désirée. Miss Yerberry would accept him if he appeared before her in a postilion's smock. Her mother would see to that.

How sordid it all was. Here was he with an illustrious title and no money. And there was Miss Yerberry with money and no title. Like two pieces of a jigsaw waiting to be fitted together.

My lord was getting moody again . . .

Stanton saw his eyes darken. 'Don't you go getting blue-devilled again, sir,' he begged. 'I know this house is in mourning but, from the atmosphere just lately, you'd think somebody else had died.'

'Perhaps somebody has,' Hugo replied. 'Me.'

Stanton was shocked. 'Don't say so! You, a soldier, tempting fate like that. You know you must not do so!'

'I am no longer a soldier,' Hugo pointed out. 'As for fate, why, I've played with it all my life. It revenges itself now by playing with me.'

'I don't like to hear you talk like this,' Stanton fretted.

'Perhaps I've talked too much, and indiscreetly.' Hugo looked questioningly at Stanton.

'You've spoken to a pair of ears and not a flapping mouth,' his valet protested indignantly. 'You can trust me, my lord, and it grieves me that you should question it.'

'Forgive me, Stanton,' Hugo said immediately. 'I don't think I am quite myself. You must know that had I ever had any doubts about your discretion I would not have bought you out of the army with me.'

Mollified, Stanton said no more and the Earl left his bedchamber. It was not always easy to serve Hugo but it was rapidly being brought home to Stanton that it was not necessarily easy to be an earl, either.

Hugo's mind was running along the same lines as he sipped sherry in the blue saloon, which adjoined the dining-room downstairs. He had developed a liking for sherry during the campaigns in Spain but he had no time to savour a second glass before Jamieson entered to announce that dinner was served.

It was eight o'clock precisely. Two footmen opened the double doors to the dining-room and Hugo found himself walking through whether he was ready or not.

He took his place in the carved chair at the head of the huge table and accepted portions from several of the dishes that were offered to him.

Mrs Barrow had put herself to little trouble since the Earl was dining alone, but the Soup à la Reine and her special way with baked cod found favour with him. He also had a generous helping of plovers' eggs, and called for more before tackling the roast sirloin of beef with creamed potatoes and spinach. The fricassee of chicken, glazed ham and pancakes were dismissed but Hugo enjoyed a peach grown in his own hothouses in Hampshire before turning his attention to slivers of toasts spread with goose pâté. Then he waved away the claret and called for brandy. He had but one glass, however, before rising from the table.

He told Jamieson that he was setting out on foot to White's immediately. This message was passed on so swiftly that Stanton contrived to be standing by the front door by the time Hugo reached the hall.

He accepted the black gloves that Stanton handed to him, the only visible sign that he was in mourning. Hugo felt they were a sufficient mark of respect, since Harry would have been the first to denounce prolonged observance of his passing as nothing less than morbid.

Stanton set a cape over Hugo's shoulders and handed him his high-crowned hat. When this was settled to Hugo's satisfaction, his valet gave him his cane, bowed and nodded to the footman stationed by the front door.

Hugo passed through the smartly opened door, went down the steps outside his mansion and strolled through the velvet evening towards his club. He felt close in spirit to those aristocrats who had ridden in tumbrels through the streets of Paris for a fatal meeting with Madame la Guillotine—save no crowds jeered him.

Hugo was mocked only by himself. And it was only too likely that he would survive his encounter with Mrs Yerberry.

How he detested matchmaking mamas! But how desperately he needed the goodwill of this one . . .

Hugo entered White's, where he was promptly surrounded by friends he hadn't seen in an age. They were good, lively fellows. They did not get maudling about Harry, merely bringing Hugo up to date on all the *on-dits* he was likely to be interested in.

He kept to himself the fact that he would shortly become the hottest *on-dit* of all, once this evening's work was done.

After an hour or so he left the club and sauntered towards the Yerberry mansion. He declined to summon any of the hackney carriages that passed, since some perverse imp within him was still prompting him to delay.

What did he expect? A fortune to drop out of that star-strewn sky so that he might be delivered from Isabelle and her mama?

Hugo thought of the mortgages to be redeemed, of the money needed to rectify the years of neglect his estates had suffered. He thought, too, of his cottagers, many of whom—if his steward was to be believed—were in danger of their humble dwellings collapsing about their ears.

Harry, it seemed, had never laid out one penny on anything but his gaming debts. The peculiar code of honour by which all gentlemen lived demanded that, though tradesmen might be allowed to starve, debts incurred over the gaming tables must be promptly settled—even if one had to borrow to do so.

And Harry had borrowed, and borrowed again, until the curst moneylenders had him firmly in their grasp. He had never had any head for cards, nor the shrewdness to perceive he had not, but he had been reared to hold on to his land.

He had reacted with wrath when his agent had suggested that the lesser estates should be sold off to support the principal seat of the Devershams, and had refused point blank to do so.

This, in time, would prove a blessing if Hugo could get them safely out of the creditors' hands. The estates, reorganised and modernised, would yield sufficient profits within a few years to enrich the title once more.

It was not this task which daunted Hugo, it was the means he had to employ to begin it. That was why he loitered.

Anger and contempt at his own self-pity spurred Hugo on. Within a few minutes he was approaching the Yerberry house, the lighted flambeaux outside proclaiming that entertainment was being provided within.

He entered swiftly. Mrs Yerberry had long since abandoned her hostess's position at the foot of the stairs but Hugo scarcely had time to seek her out before she pounced on him.

She was all purple crêpe, ostrich feathers and smiles. She was also too gushing in her welcome. Hugo repressed a shudder and steeled himself. He had delivered himself into Mrs Yerberry's hands. She would do the rest.

His handsome face like a frozen mask, he wondered if he would ever find it within himself to be grateful for the Yerberry fortune.

CHAPTER
SIX

MRS YERBERRY knew the instant she set eyes on Hugo's lean and masculine figure that all she had heard of the Deversham financial débâcle was fact, and her hopes soared to dizzy heights. Isabelle would be a countess! Why else would Hugo grace her soirée?

'My dear boy, what a delightful surprise,' she cooed, extending her plump hand. 'How enchanting of you to flatter us with your presence.'

Damned toad-eater, Hugo thought, smiling with lips so stiff they scarcely seemed his own. 'You overestimate the value of my company,' he replied, bowing over her be-ringed fingers.

'La, such a tease!' The ostrich feathers set in her tightly-curled hair swayed precariously as she nodded her head coyly at him. He tried not to flinch as she grasped his arm and went on: 'I am relieved to see you looking so well, Hugo. I heard you were wounded at Waterloo, like so many of our dear, valiant boys.'

'The veriest scratch,' he assured her.

'So brave,' she gushed. 'So brave!'

Hugo began to be bored, but he said politely: 'If that is so, then I have my reward in surviving to enjoy such dazzling company.'

Mrs Yerberry furled her fan of lace—and more ostrich feathers—and tapped him playfully on the shoulder. 'You are trying to put me out of countenance, you naughty boy.'

A barely concealed shudder ran through Hugo's frame, but fortunately Mrs Yerberry was turning to lead him into a room from which came the strains of music, and so did not notice it.

'For once I'm pleased to admit we do not have a crush,' she went on as he fell into step beside her. 'A boon, you will admit, on such a hot night—although I know nothing will keep you young people from dancing.'

Hugo, knowing he was being commanded to dance with her daughter, quite forgot to smile. The devil take his pride! If he did not watch out, it would be as much his undoing as gambling had been Harry's. He had forced himself to come here, but already he was wishing he could escape.

Mrs Yerberry, shrewdly divining that her soirée would not attract sufficient company to merit the use of the ballroom, had installed the musicians in the largest of her saloons. It was good strategy for the few couples now dancing contrived to make the room look respectably filled.

Hugo, pausing in the doorway, was unaware of how arrogant he looked as he allowed his bored eyes to roam over the dancers. He found it easy enough to spot Isabelle, since she was a smaller but scarcely thinner version of her mother. The same light red hair—almost pink!—that had a distressing habit of fuzzing out of its carefully curled ringlets.

Hugo told himself wearily that it was just like him to notice first what was unquestionably Isabelle's worst feature. The rest of her was more acceptable. Blue eyes, clear complexion, well-formed lips and a retroussé nose that made her round face appealing enough. She was not pretty, but neither was she, as the delectable Désirée thought, precisely plain.

Perhaps her yellow gown was not the wisest choice for a plump girl with pinkish hair, but it was not her fault that her mother lacked an eye for colour and her own opinion was never sought. Isabelle's hands and feet were small and so were her ambitions, but she was ruled by her mother. Not having an assertive personality, she was easily intimidated. If Mrs Yerberry had not exerted herself on her daughter's behalf, Isabelle would never have done so.

She was poles apart from Désirée, and Dominga she would never have understood at all. The sole object of Isabelle's life was to please her mama, but though she was weak she was not a fool. When she saw Hugo, she knew why he was here.

How clever her mama was! She had predicted that they

would be receiving a visit from the new Earl of Deversham. Isabelle, well drilled, knew that she must not let this handsome prize slip through her fingers so she obediently caught her mother's eye. Receiving the summons she expected, she walked over to where Mrs Yerberry stood with Hugo.

Isabelle acknowledged the Earl's bow with a hasty curtsy. There was always an air of anxiety about Isabelle, engendered by her fear of displeasing her mother. This anxiety caused her to fidget and flush as Hugo looked down at her.

He could not fail to notice, and good breeding compelled him to talk lightly on matters of no importance while she recovered her composure. Isabelle, however, only looked increasingly uncomfortable. Hugo's hopes of her, never very high, sank into oblivion. She would never make a countess. She would be better off buried in the country with some unassuming squire. Well, perhaps she could be persuaded to stay at Deversham Hall for the better part of the year. Oh, damnation! Her mother wouldn't allow that. She would want to see Isabelle at all the glittering Society functions, and Hugo had a feeling she would make a pest of herself to achieve her own ends. But he must proceed regardless if his estates were to be saved . . .

When the orchestra struck up a waltz, he asked Isabelle if he might have the pleasure. She muttered something which he took to be an acceptance and he led her on to the floor.

Isabelle, he discovered, danced well enough but with no flair. She kept her eyes fixed resolutely on a button on his waistcoat. Though the thought of such a handsome bridegroom had caused her heart to flutter, now that his strong arms were about her she felt strangely oppressed. The replies she gave to Hugo's conversational gambits were monosyllabic and largely inaudible. It was a sad fact that Isabelle when she particularly wanted to please was incapable of it.

Hugo was exasperated. The dance over, he restored Isabelle to her mother and danced with two other young ladies. When another waltz commenced, he danced with Isabelle again. Two waltzes with her in one evening was as good a sign as any of his determination to fix his interest with her. He had done his duty and shown his hand, but self-disgust hardened his face into a mask which Isabelle took to be indifference.

She wasn't to know that, as he whirled around the floor with her and looked down at her fuzzy pink head, he pitied her almost as much as he pitied himself. Poor Isabelle. She was nothing more than a pawn between her mother's ambition and an earl's poverty. She would be moved swiftly from a betrothal to a wedding, and away on a honeymoon, without ever having had a say in the game at all.

Hugo found himself wondering what Désirée was doing now. His steps faltered, causing Isabelle to stumble. He steadied her. 'I beg your pardon,' he murmured. 'I—' He broke off. He could not admit that his attention had wandered. He wished to please the girl, not humiliate her.

'My army service has made me a little out of practice,' he lied.

Unfortunately, Isabelle was not green enough to believe him. She had had her share of young officers dangling after her, and she knew it was impossible for a former dashing Hussar captain to forget the steps of the most popular dance of the day.

She stammered a suitable reply, but her spirits drooped. It was clear she had not impressed the Earl. Mama would be furious. At this alarming thought, her shoulders also drooped.

Hugo noticed. 'Isabelle?' he questioned, as pity for her stirred in him again. 'Would you rather sit out the remainder of the dance? I could fetch you a glass of lemonade.'

She glanced fearfully at him. There were too many candles burning for a hot night and her face shone from heat, exertion and anxiety. 'No!' she replied, with something akin to panic. 'That is . . . very happy to be dancing, you see.'

Hugo did not see at all. 'Are you sure?'

'Positive.' Isabelle's head nodded frantically. In her agitation, she stumbled of her own accord. Again Hugo steadied her. She hid her face, now the colour of her hair, against his coat.

Hugo repressed a sigh. He had given up a goddess for a clodpole. Once more a vision of the fair creature who teased his dreams and taunted his daytime hours rose before his eyes. Oh, Désirée! A groan, swiftly smothered, almost broke from his lips.

But suddenly the physical and mental anguish he suffered through his need for her was blotted out as the full cunning of her strategy burst upon him. The little minx had known he would be bored out of his mind after one minute of Isabelle's company, and that his thoughts could not help but remain with the true object of his desire. He laughed aloud, for Désirée was a woman to appreciate, as well as love.

Mrs Yerberry, watching him, was in high gig. She saw and heard that laugh and thought that her daughter was succeeding in entertaining him.

But that confused maiden, casting a hunted look at Hugo, was more puzzled than hopeful, and only prayed that he wasn't laughing at her. She was relieved when the dance ended and he took his leave.

Hugo went over to his hostess and thanked her for her hospitality, but Mrs Yerberry wasn't finished with him yet.

'I'd hoped you might stay a little longer,' she told him pointedly, 'but Isabelle and I will be at home to morning callers.'

Hugo's proud spirit rebelled at what was little more than an order. 'Indeed?' he drawled. 'I fear I'm never abroad so early.'

But Mrs Yerberry, knowing full well his circumstances and scenting victory, was not to be thwarted. She suggested firmly: 'An effort could perhaps be made?'

The urge to snub her almost overwhelmed the Earl. He struggled with himself until, finally, prudence won. 'Perhaps.' He bowed with cold correctness and left.

Mrs Yerberry was not to be deterred by his hauteur. It was, after all, to be expected. But she was sure that, having come to heel once, he would do so again. How gratifying it would be when she could say to her cronies: 'My daughter—the Countess, you know . . .'

With this pleasant picture in her mind, she showered her daughter with congratulations she did not feel to be premature.

Isabelle was bewildered. She was sure Hugo had not

liked her, even hoped that he had not, for the more she thought of him the more he frightened her. She knew he had tried to be kind, but she was quite overpowered by a quality within him which she could not quite define. What was it that had frightened her? A feeling of power? Almost, dare she think it, of ruthlessness? Were these the things that set him apart from the rest of her suitors?

Isabelle had visited a menagerie once, and for some reason this sprang to her mind as she considered Hugo. The animals had been safely confined and yet they had prowled their cages with unceasing restlessness. Brooding, inscrutable, wholly savage.

Isabelle had known they could not hurt her, but she had felt threatened. She had shaken so much that her exasperated mother had taken her away.

The parallel with the Earl was absurd, yet the thought came unbidden that if Hugo were stripped of his noble trappings he might have much in common with those savage beasts. Exquisite breeding disguised him, good manners confined him, but within him she sensed the same kind of dangerous restlessness.

Not given to profound thinking at the best of times, Isabelle was quite overcome. She began to shiver.

Her mother, in the middle of describing the illustrious future awaiting her daughter, stopped abruptly. 'Whatever is the matter with you, child? Are you not pleased?'

'Mama, he frightens me!' Isabelle blurted out.

'Frightens you?' Mrs Yerberry repeated blankly. 'What nonsense is this?'

'He makes me feel oppressed,' Isabelle confessed, unable to think of any other way of describing the primitive fears the Earl evoked in her.

Mrs Yerberry was about to demolish her daughter with a few well-chosen words when she suddenly perceived what it was that had Isabelle in such a quake. It was fear of the bridal bed. That was natural enough, of course, but the Earl would know how to cope with it, as all men did. It was not a mother's province. Still, she spoke more kindly to Isabelle and said that tomorrow afternoon they would drive to Bond Street and order a new gown or two for her, and perhaps purchase some bonnets. Fondly imagining that she had diverted her daughter with promised treats, she didn't for a moment suspect that Isabelle's thoughts had faltered far short of the bridal bed.

Violence, as it happened, was the prime emotion surging through Hugo as he strode towards Grosvenor Square. As always when his pride was wounded, he felt an urge to lash out. It mattered little whether it were with words or fists but, being denied any kind of outlet, he seethed.

He disliked Isabelle and he loathed her mother. And his amusement at Désirée's ploy to land him with such an insipid bride was veering sharply to rage. If Désirée loved him, how could she so coldly plot his future? Clearly she did not wish him to be happy in his marriage, and yet he couldn't find it in him to wish her unhappy in hers. Whatever happened, he could not bear to think of her miserable. Yet she had been ready to push him into the most miserable existence possible, and it was for this reason that he seethed.

To be married to Isabelle would be intolerable, to have Mrs Yerberry as a relative would be insufferable, but to have Désirée on the sidelines deftly manipulating the situation to her own advantage was more than flesh and blood could stand.

Oh, god! How he wished he was a Hussar captain still, fighting a tangible enemy when there was one before him, and wining and womanising when there was not. That was the real life for a man such as himself.

Hugo changed direction and went to Watier's, where he drank and gambled more deeply than usual. Some onlookers muttered that he was bent on following his brother to the devil, but since the Earl rose from the tables at three in the morning several hundred pounds the richer, this observation was scarcely justified. Harry would have gambled until dawn, and he would have lost.

Surprisingly, Hugo was stone cold sober when he reached Deversham House. It was as if the alcohol he had consumed could make no headway against his anger.

After three hours' sleep, he was up again and shouting for Stanton to bring his shaving water. By the time the early morning sun was filtering into his bed-chamber, Hugo had left it. His impatience was not so much to get this day started as to forget the one which had preceded it.

Stanton had sent a message down to the stables, which ensured that the Earl was not kept waiting for his horse as he left the house. Hearing that Hugo was in a black mood, Parsons had brought round Sebastian, a mottled-looking black stallion which had been purchased in Spain. He was a large and unlovely animal, a horsey equivalent of a mongrel, and an odd choice of mount for an aristocrat.

There was a good understanding between horse and master, however, and Sebastian was the only one of Hugo's four mounts at Waterloo which had survived the day.

The horse stood placidly awaiting events without any of the snorting and nervous prancing that distinguished a thoroughbred, but the moment Hugo was in the saddle his lassitude vanished. The streets were almost empty at this hour and it wasn't long before the Town was left behind and Sebastian was able to lengthen his stride into a gallop that ate up the miles.

Hugo's only aim was to find sufficient space in which to gallop away his still-simmering rage. When he turned back for Town, he thought wryly how simple his pleasures had become, but he had recovered some measure of his resignation towards the blows that fate had dealt him.

When he reached Deversham House he was more than ready for his breakfast and the frothing tankard of ale which was set before him.

By keeping his mind off the call he must make on Mrs Yerberry and Isabelle later in the morning, he was able to relish a sirloin steak heaped with eggs, which Mrs Barrows knew was his favourite breakfast. The servants, as usual, were doing their best to sweeten his mood.

When Hugo was ready to leave the table, he filled his tankard afresh from the jug at his elbow and carried it into the library. There he settled at his desk to read the morning papers before tackling again the business of the estate.

It was as he drained the tankard a few minutes later that he read in the Gazette the announcement of a betrothal between Désirée Louise de Lafayeure and Augustus Percival Marsham.

With a smothered oath, Hugo crushed the paper and

hurled it from him. Désirée had wasted no time. The hasty announcement of her engagement seemed nothing short of a cold-blooded insult.

Heaven knew he had not wished her to languish in tears, but he had thought she would allow a few days to elapse before committing herself to another man. Surely their love deserved that much!

The chagrin Hugo felt at Désirée's precipitate action went some way towards quelling the anguish the announcement had caused him since the blow to his heart had been deflected by his pride. He became at that moment precisely what Isabelle, who depended on instinct rather than reasoning, had suspected—he was a very dangerous animal indeed.

Jamieson had no knowledge of this as he tapped on the library door and awaited permission to enter. This being granted, he made his dignified way to where the Earl sat at his desk.

'What is it?' Hugo asked.

Such was the controlled calm in his voice that Jamieson paused, alarmed. He saw the cold glitter in Hugo's eyes and glanced involuntarily at the tankard.

It could not be the ale, though, and there was no sign of stronger liquor. Partly reassured, Jamieson advanced until he stood by the desk. 'Mr Horace Ponting is desirous of an interview with you, my lord.'

'What makes you suppose I might be interested in the desires of a man I have never heard of?'

'He called yesterday, you will remember.'

'You delude yourself,' Hugo said coldly.

The new golden guineas residing in his pocket prompted Jamieson to persevere with: 'I brought him to your attention when you returned from Wimbledon.'

'And what did I say?'

'You consigned him to the devil,' Jamieson admitted.

'Then I showed more sense than you are at this moment,' Hugo snapped.

'I felt it my duty,' Jamieson returned bravely, 'to remind you that he called on a matter to your advantage.'

'And yours?' his master guessed shrewdly. 'How much has he bribed you to annoy me in this manner?'

Jamieson allowed his gaunt features to register outrage as he replied stiffly: 'I would feel I was failing in my duty, my lord, if I did not apprise you of a matter which might prove beneficial to you.'

'You know what,' Hugo said, leaning back in his chair, 'there are times when you're a damned sight more noble than I am—or so you would have me believe. What a pity I already know you for the slippery devil you are!'

'Now, now, my lord,' Jamieson cautioned. 'You know I always have your best interests at heart.'

'We could debate that point all morning,' Hugo returned dryly. Then, with a suddenly reckless air, he pushed the papers on his desk aside. 'Very well. I will see this Ponting, on condition he is willing to risk being thrown into the street if his business is not to my liking.'

Jamieson bowed and retreated. Like the Earl, he thought Mr Ponting would choose to withdraw intact, but this did not prove to be so. Mr Ponting was willing to hazard life and limb in pursuit of his five hundred guineas, although he felt no little trepidation when he found himself closeted in the library with the Earl a short while later.

Hugo was sprawled in his chair at the desk, looking most relaxed, and yet Mr Ponting noticed the wild glitter in his eyes. He could not quite shake the feeling that he was confronting a cornered animal about to spring, and he jumped when Hugo said: 'No doubt you will acquaint me with your business at your leisure.'

The sarcasm in his voice caused Mr Ponting to bow belatedly but deeply. 'It is a most delicate matter, my lord,' he began, thinking what a splendid foil this aristocrat's fair-haired handsomeness would make for the heiress's dark-haired beauty.

What little interest Hugo felt in Mr Ponting died. 'Another female to be bought off? I'm dashed if I know how my brother found the time to sire so many brats,' he said carelessly.

'Not a matter of that kind,' Mr Ponting disclaimed instantly.

'There was no issue? Or are you suggesting he gave a respectable female a slip on the shoulder? Neither sounds like my brother, so you'd best be warned that I'm no chicken for easy plucking.'

'No, no, it is not that sort of business at all,' Mr Ponting reiterated, his carefully-rehearsed speech forgotten.

'You said it was a delicate matter. What the deuce else could it be?' Hugo demanded irritably.

'If you will permit me to explain . . .' Mr Ponting beseeched.

Hugo waved him towards a chair. 'Then for god's sake sit down and get on with it, man.'

Mr Ponting sat down gratefully. 'The delicate matter I refer to, my lord, is—is—your marriage.'

'The devil it is!' Hugo snapped.

Mr Ponting hurried on: 'Forgive my presumption, but I am acting on behalf of a lady who naturally cannot bring herself to your attention.'

'You waste your time. I am not shopping for a Cit's daughter,' Hugo told him contemptuously.

It was as Mr Ponting had feared. The great hurdle which he had hoped to circumvent last had loomed up first. He summoned up his dignity and replied: 'I speak of a great heiress.'

'Trade is dealt with in my agent's office. It does not intrude into the family bed-chambers,' the Earl replied disdainfully.

'Quite so,' Mr Ponting agreed ingratiatingly. 'Generally speaking, business and family are best kept apart, but I dare to believe that this particular young lady might prove to be a bridge between the two.'

'Lady?' Heavy sarcasm filled the Earl's voice. 'Who do you think you are fooling? And as for bridges, I've crossed many in my time but fastidiousness compels me to turn aside from this one.'

Mr Ponting felt his arrogance as positively as he felt his own sweat on his brow, but he repeated firmly: 'Lady, my lord. Unquestionably a lady.'

Hugo's eyebrows rose, his disbelief apparent.

'She is the daughter of a deceased Spanish gentlewoman,' Mr Ponting avowed, 'and a relative through her step-mama of Sir Piers Reverson, of the Kent Reversons.'

Hugo picked up a quill and toyed with it. 'Her father?' he asked, guessing where the rub lay.

'Deceased also. He was Wilfrid Browne, esquire, truly the most respected man of business the City has ever known.' Mr Ponting was pleased with his choice of words. 'Respected' was the truth, and it implied respectability.

'A Cit, in fact, and you think I would look at his daughter?' Hugo laughed in a way that would have made Dominga's blood boil had she heard him. He picked up a knife and began to sharpen the end of the quill, adding: 'I advise you to try a needy baronet. You should find one who is not too fussy who he allows under the family sheets provided the dowry is large enough.'

It was no comfort to Mr Ponting to have the advice he had given Miss Romero-Browne repeated by the Earl, albeit in a blunter way, but he would not allow himself to be deterred. 'While we are speaking of dowries, my lord, permit me to mention that this young lady's would be fifty thousand pounds.'

The Earl laughed again. 'You are out of your league, Ponting. I would expect that sum from a real lady.'

Mr Ponting bit his lip. 'The matter could be debated, my lord.'

Hugo flung quill and knife back on to the desk. 'If you are a shrewd man, you will consider the matter closed. I am not noted for my patience and I'm quite capable of—er—depositing you in the street. God knows I've had no sport for days!'

'I beg you will not act over-hastily. This lady has great beauty!'

'Tell me an heiress who hasn't,' Hugo replied cynically.

Mr Ponting knew he had to do something, and quickly, to save his skin and his commission. He had not been idle since he had been in Dominga's employ, however, and he decided to use the gossip he had gleaned about the Earl in one last desperate gambit. He said boldly: 'She is lovelier than Mademoiselle Lafayeure and richer than Miss Yerberry.'

'You meddle too deep in my business.' Hugo's tone was soft but he looked more dangerous than ever and Mr Ponting resigned himself as best he could to the indignity of being hurled out of this haughty nobleman's house.

Indeed, such had been Hugo's intention, but through his anger at this plump Cit's presumption came an idea that made him pause. He settled back in his chair and studied Mr Ponting.

Was it possible that this little man was placing in his hands a weapon with which he could pay back the blows dealt to his pride by Désirée and Mrs Yerberry? If so, what splendid justice that would be, and far more sport than removing Mr Ponting in a violent fashion. He asked sharply: 'The heiress's name?'

'Miss Dominga Romero-Browne.' Mr Ponting did not know what had saved him, but his relief was profound. It brought another outbreak of perspiration to his already damp brow.

Hugo frowned: 'A devilishly odd name. I thought you said her father's name was merely Browne?'

'Ah, but her mother came from a good family and so her name was added to Browne in the way that has lately become fashionable.'

'H'm. In my world a worthy name will always stand by itself, and Dominga, dash it, is Spanish for Sunday.'

Mr Ponting was startled. Odd, indeed, to name a girl after a day of the week, but her mother was foreign, after all, and there was never any telling what strange things foreigners might do. 'A child born on the Sabbath is held to be comely and of good disposition,' he pointed out.

'And is that true of this, shall we say, lady?'

Mentally reviewing the audacious Miss Romero-Browne, Mr Ponting replied diplomatically: 'I observed nothing in her to the contrary.'

'The size of her fortune?' Hugo asked.

This was safer ground. Mr Ponting beamed as he replied: 'Two hundred thousand pounds readily disposable and an income from investments of no less than thirty thousand pounds a year, possibly a great deal more, particularly now the end of the war will bring a boom in foreign trade.'

Hugo was startled. That knocked the Yerberry money into a cocked hat and tempted him at least to view this unknown heiress.

Mr Ponting pressed home his advantage by drawing a

sheaf of papers from his pocket and placing them before the Earl. 'These contain personal and financial details of Miss Romero-Browne, so that your lawyers will be able to satisfy themselves that all her claims are true.'

'That would come later,' Hugo said, pushing the papers aside, 'provided that I find her at least bearable. She has the look of a lady?'

'My lord,' Mr Ponting replied, laying his hand over his heart, 'she *is* a lady.'

Hugo smiled. 'Pray determine how much of a lady she is when you tell her that I would not consider her hand for less than half her principal and all of her yearly income.'

Since husbands normally took control of their wives' assets, there was nothing unusual in the Earl's terms, but Mr Ponting had to say: 'The terms of her father's Will dictate that her invested fortune must remain in her hands, my lord.'

'Then it appears our business is concluded,' Hugo said. 'I'll have no woman holding the purse-strings in my household.'

'If you would only agree to meet the young lady you would see for yourself that she is everything that is admirable,' Mr Ponting pleaded. 'Many connoisseurs of feminine excellence would deem a dowry an unnecessary inducement to marriage, 'pon my word they would.'

'She must be a paragon,' Hugo replied cynically. He was not carried away by Mr Ponting's fervour, but neither had he lost the notion that if this heiress was pretty and presentable he could pay back Désirée for trying to saddle him with Isabelle. And if she was as rich as Mr Ponting avowed, he would snap his fingers at the encroaching Mrs Yerberry . . .

He would confound everyone, by Jupiter, including those idle gentlemen who must now be placing their bets on how soon the Earl of Deversham would be leg-shackled to Miss Yerberry. It appealed to Hugo.

Nothing in his autocratic life had prepared him for dancing to other people's tunes, and to be able to call the moves again was just the salve his smarting pride needed. The Romero-Browne chit, providing he did not hold her in aversion, also offered the advantage of a private arrangement. No more humiliating dangling after an heiress in public!

Curse Harry! How he would laugh if he knew of Hugo's forbearance with the Yerberry mama. Well, he would not have been amused if he could have known that his expensive dissipations had opened the Deversham door to a Cit's daughter.

'Is she very vulgar?' he asked. 'Bearing in mind that your idea of vulgarity and mine might be vastly different.'

'Rest assured, my lord, that I would not affront you by introducing you to a person who in any way smelled of the shop.'

'Why me?' Hugo asked.

'The young lady wishes to be a countess.'

'Any countess?' Hugo exclaimed.

'As to that, my lord, the young lady must speak for herself.'

'Is she capable of it?'

'Indubitably. Miss Romero-Browne is extremely articulate.'

That was an improvement on Isabelle, but it could be carried to the extreme. 'Loose-jawed, is she?' Hugo asked.

'Not in the least. Everything she says is to the point.'

'Dammit, I've never met such a woman,' Hugo scoffed.

'Then you must not deny yourself the pleasure of meeting Miss Romero-Browne,' Mr Ponting replied triumphantly.

Hugo regarded him consideringly for several moments, then Mr Ponting pointed out: 'You have nothing to lose.'

'That is the only statement you have made so far that I can accept without question. For the rest, we shall see when I meet this—this—lady you champion.'

Mr Ponting was overjoyed. He had secured the interview and he was already one hundred guineas the richer. All that remained now was to arrange a time when Miss Romero-Browne could be brought here to meet the Earl. Quite moved by gratitude, he promised: 'You will not regret it, my lord.'

'I wonder? Where does she live?'

'Chersey Manor in Surrey, no great distance from Town.'

'She is there now?'

'Yes, my lord.'

'Awaiting events, no doubt,' Hugo mused. 'We must not disappoint her.' He went over to the bell-pull and tugged at it. When Jamieson appeared, he said: 'I shall want my curricle in fifteen minutes and I shall not be home for lunch.'

Jamieson, his mind seething with possibilities, bowed and withdrew.

Mr Ponting was a little confused so he said conversationally: 'You make a journey, my lord?'

'*We* make a journey, Mr Ponting,' Hugo corrected him.

'We? How can that be? I mean, where?' Mr Ponting asked, consternation casting a shadow over the warm glow of success he had been basking in.

'Chersey Manor. Where else?'

Mr Ponting was taken aback. 'Would it not be better if we arranged for the young lady to come here? We cannot just call in on her, my lord. She is not expecting us.'

'Precisely.' Hugo's eyes were glittering again. 'I wish to see this Miss Romero-Browne when she is all unprepared. I am—or was—a soldier and I know the value of an unexpected raid. There's no better way of exposing an enemy's weaknesses.'

'The enemy?' Mr Ponting faltered, and thought it strange that the Earl and Miss Romero-Browne should think along the same lines when contemplating their proposed marriage partners. His romantic soul, which clung to his rosy vision of a love-match, received a severe jolt and prompted him to repeat: 'Enemy?'

'Are not all women enemies at one time or another?' Hugo walked over to a side-table, selected a decanter and poured his best Malaga into two glasses. He gave one to Mr Ponting and went on: 'I give you a toast. Confusion to the enemy. That is why we go to Chersey Manor immediately, Mr—what the devil did you say your name was?'

'Ponting,' Mr Ponting replied weakly, regarding the liquid in his glass as if it were deadly poison. To drink to such a toast would be like drinking to the doom of all the heiress's aspirations . . . to say nothing of his own five hundred guineas.

'Well, drink up, man,' Hugo urged, then laughed like a man whose cares had temporarily fallen from him. 'Think what famous sport it might be to take this Cit's daughter by surprise. Damme, I've a notion we'll soon find out how much of a lady she is or whether, as I suspect, it's all a sham.'

CHAPTER
SEVEN

DOMINGA looked every inch the lady as she rode back to Chersey Manor just before ten that same morning, and nobody would have supposed that she could possibly be anybody's enemy. Indeed, she seemed something of a latter-day Diana on her skittish grey mare, save that she had not been hunting. She had merely been out riding, as had Hugo, to ease a certain restlessness of spirit.

She was wearing a stylish bottle-green riding habit, and a dashing little hat with a swept-back feather was propped on top of her coiled raven hair. There was a petulant droop to her full lips, however, for she wanted action.

How long would it be before she heard from Horace Ponting? How long before the noble Earl of Deversham would be forced to swallow, bit by choking bit, his insufferable pride? Dominga, anxious for events to move towards a conclusion, shifted restlessly in her side-saddle. Her thoroughbred mare, Melody, responded by throwing up her head and rearing nervously.

Big Sam Gibbons, riding behind her on a huge seventeen-hand gelding, urged his horse level with Dominga's but resisted the impulse to put a restraining hand on Melody's bridle. A cut across the wrist from his mistress's riding crop would be all he would receive for his protectiveness. He knew well enough that Dominga could quieten her horse unaided, but the impulse was hard to suppress. He had been looking after her for so long that it was difficult to know how, or when, to stop.

When Dominga had her mare under control, she said affably: 'I would have whipped you, Gibbons, had you dared.'

Gibbons chuckled. They knew each other so well that few things needed explaining between them. He allowed her to draw ahead again for they were entering Chersey

Wood and the path was not wide enough for two horses. It was a curious and unorthodox relationship that existed between them, but both had had good cause to be grateful to it over the years.

It had been in this very wood, some ten years previously, that Sam Gibbons had been engaged in a little moonlight poaching when he had walked into an ambush set by two of Wilfrid Browne's gamekeepers. The speed with which Gibbons had taken to his heels had been remarkable in so large a fellow, and he would have made good his escape had not one gamekeeper shot the other in the confusion of the moment.

Hearing the man's anguished screams, Gibbons had paused. His lively curiosity, reinforced by his hungry need to recover the rabbit he had dropped, had prompted him to creep back through the trees. He had watched the inept attempts of the gamekeeper who had loosed his shot so recklessly to staunch the flow of blood from his colleague's chest. Nothing in Gibbons's life had led him to suppose he owed his fellow man anything, but he was a criminal by need rather than by nature and so he had gone forward.

Thrusting aside the panicky gamekeeper, he had bent over the wounded one. Then, tearing his own already ragged shirt into strips, he had competently bound the wound and stopped the man bleeding to death.

Since the uninjured gamekeeper was slightly built and deeply shocked, it had also fallen to Gibbons to carry the wounded man back to the Manor.

He faced, at best, transportation to Botany Bay for his troubles. But Wilfrid Browne, when the story was recounted to him, had thought that such a fate would be a shameful waste of a strong and resourceful man. The sort of man he stood in need of . . . He had questioned Gibbons closely and received frank answers, though Gibbons was surprised that the squire should be interested in his life story.

Gibbons had run away to sea as a boy and served for several years on a merchantman. When this had palled, he had worked in a Portsmouth hostelry until, having twice fought his way free of press-gangs, he had travelled inland. He had turned his hand to whatever jobs were available but when none were poaching had proved as good a way as any of keeping body and soul together.

Wilfrid had listened carefully and decided that here was the very man he needed to protect his daughter—from herself rather than any other hazard—for although Dominga was but seven at this time she had already shown her wild blood could not be entirely tamed.

Her father understood only too well why she was seized from time to time by an urge to wander, but it worried him how often she managed to give the slip to the guardians set about her. Her step-mama, groom, maid and governess—all had failed to predict when her wild moods were coming upon her—but this man Gibbons, Wilfrid reasoned, might fare better if he were made responsible for Dominga's safety outside the house.

Only two days previously Dominga had disappeared at dusk and Wilfrid had found her sitting at a gipsy camp-fire in the wood with only her fine clothes to distinguish her from the motley crowd of horse-dealers, peg-makers and fortune-tellers, whose supper she was sharing. It was not surprising that the chill that had clutched at Wilfrid's heart at such a sight should still be with him when he interviewed the poacher, or that he should feel Dominga needed a guardian who would be up to all her wily tricks.

Gibbons, toughened by the harsh buffetings of fate into expecting no mercy from the squire, had been stunned by the proposition Wilfrid had then put to him. In return for no charges being laid against him, he would enter Wilfrid's employ to guard Miss Dominga, and to accompany her everywhere she went outside the house. He would receive board, lodging, clothes and a yearly stipend above that of a more conventional footman. It was like coming across an oasis in a desert, and Gibbons had scarcely been able to believe his good fortune.

As for Dominga, once she had been told that she could wander where she pleased provided that Gibbons was with her, she tolerated his presence. This tolerance swiftly turned to friendship, for Gibbons knew so many and such unlikely things. Moreover, he readily discussed subjects with her that would cause the other servants to throw up their hands in horror.

With his escort, she enjoyed freedom without any of the scolds that were the aftermath of her illicit trips from the house. As a result, she became more biddable over the matter of her lessons.

What's more, Wilfrid was able to congratulate himself that he had hit upon the very way to control Dominga's waywardness. Neither he nor Gibbons were ever aware that, as she grew older, Dominga also grew clever enough to hoodwink the pair of them whenever she had a mind to.

Now, as Gibbons rode behind Dominga through Chersey Wood, he knew that he was nearing the end of his employment at the Manor.

Wilfrid Browne, whose nature it had been to part fools from their money without the slightest twinge of conscience, had none the less believed in rewarding those who had served him well. Thus it was that under the terms of his Will, Gibbons would inherit sufficient money once Dominga was married to buy the small hostelry that had always been the sum total of his desires. There could be no luckier man in the world, he told himself, as they passed through the small clearing in the wood where Dominga had once supped with the gipsies.

Since he had accompanied his mistress up to London, he knew all about her schemes to throw a bridal noose about the noble Earl of Deversham, and since she was so very rich and beautiful he did not see how the knot could fail to hold. It was just a matter of time, that was all. Gibbons allowed a few dreams about his hostelry to weave themselves in his hard head, for once not chiding himself about the evils of tempting fate. He knew his mistress, and if a man could trust anything in this life, he could trust that she would get what she wanted. She wasn't her father's daughter for nothing.

But if Gibbons was a man well contented with his lot, it was not so with Dominga when they cleared the wood and cantered down the gentle slope to Chersey Manor. She had not outridden her restlessness and the petulance about her mouth had grown into a rebellious pout.

Accustomed as she was to the sight of her home from this aspect, she did not spare it a thought although the view was an extremely pretty one. Indeed, Chersey Manor, mellowed by the years and lovingly tended by its present mistress, looked as much a part of the landscape as the hedges, trees and fields that surrounded it.

Extensions added over the centuries—a stable block adjoining one end and further living quarters at the other—resulted in the Manor resembling from the rear an E shape with the centre stroke missing. The courtyard between the two wings was cobbled. Set against the walls of the building were barrels, some of which collected rainwater while others were filled with flowers.

The effect was rustic, unpretentious and wholly charming—but it would not have pleased a fashionable eye that saw virtue only in Palladian columns, perfect proportions and precisely-landscaped gardens. The appearance of the Manor from the front would also have repelled the fastidious since it seemed in imminent danger of being taken over by the riot of roses and honeysuckle that climbed the walls. Even the flowers about the driveway were not grouped for colour but apparently grew as they pleased.

The Manor looked what it was, a farm as well as a home, with barns and hayricks dotted about, pigs snuffling in the sties and chickens straying into the house whenever anybody was imprudent enough to leave a door open. But despite its haphazardness, an air of supreme self-satisfaction seemed to permeate the Manor as it nestled among the fields that had supported it for centuries.

Cecy Romero-Browne, its mistress, adored the Manor. It was the lure that had tempted her, at the advanced age of thirty-two, to accept Wilfrid's most unexpected proposal of marriage.

His courting had been abrupt and to the point. What he required, he told her, was a lady to care for his daughter and his house. If an heir should materialise, so much the better, but he would not hold it against her if there was no issue from their union.

Cecy had not known whether to be flattered or horrified by so blunt an offer. However, it was the only one that, try as he might, her brother could raise no objection to. Great as her apprehension was at becoming the wife of the clever Wilfrid, it offered her an escape from a bleak lifetime spent under her brother's thumb. And she would be mistress of

Chersey Manor, and thus the most important lady in the district.

So Cecy had taken her courage in both hands and married Wilfrid promptly, fearing that her nerve would fail if she delayed. Her brother, the minister of the Parish, was torn between rage at losing his unpaid and uncomplaining housekeeper and gratification at acquiring such an affluent relative. His prestige in the community had improved to the detriment of his home comforts.

Wilfrid had kept his word to Cecy. He had never complained at her failure to produce children. He had been content, seemingly, to have an unquestionable lady to rear Dominga. And Cecy's reward for fifteen years of managing as best she could to stay out of her husband's way had been to gain life tenancy of the manor. Only when she died would it become Dominga's.

She felt that life could offer her no more. Indeed, much as she had stood in awe of Wilfrid, she knew how extremely lucky she had been to escape endless years of bleak spinsterhood under her brother's domination.

Wilfrid, to his credit, had never bullied her, but he was so very clever that it was impossible for her not to feel a fool in his presence. Now that he was dead, she was able to like him better—even attributing to him qualities he had never possessed.

Widowhood suited her, and she bloomed.

Soon Dominga, another frighteningly clever one, would be married and Cecy would be left to preside unhindered over the domain she adored.

There had been a fraught time after Wilfrid's death when her brother had sought to re-establish his dominance over her, but Dominga, to Cecy's undying gratitude, had swiftly sent him about his business. Now in her middle years, Cecy had become a rather plump woman but she remained as amiable and pleasant-faced as ever. Since she was of the old school, and believed in correctness in everything, she was still in strict mourning. Her rustling silk dress was of unrelieved black and the dainty cap upon her grey hair was fashioned from black lace. She deplored Dominga's return to colours before the full year was up but, as ever, she had been unable to influence the headstrong girl.

Hearing now the sound she was listening for, horses' hoofs upon the cobbles, Cecy opened a latticed window and called to Dominga to make haste as breakfast was spoiling.

Dominga waved in reply, dismounted, and left Melody in Gibbons's care. Moments later she was striding into the breakfast parlour.

Throwing her riding crop and gloves on to a polished side-table, she asked: 'May I sit down in all my dirt, or must I change and eat my breakfast cold?'

Since Cecy's mood was as sunny as the morning, she replied: 'Much as I abhor the lowering of one's standards, perhaps just this once . . .'

Dominga was seated at the table before Cecy had time to finish what she had to say, and was removing the cover from a silver tureen to peer at the devilled kidneys within.

'At least remove your hat!' Cecy exclaimed, much shocked.

'The devil take it,' Dominga muttered, unpinning the offending article and tossing it towards the side-table. She missed.

'Dominga!'

'I know! I'm lowering the standards again. What a bore it is to always be so precise. Do you think, when I'm a countess, I'll be able to leave all the propriety to lesser mortals? Certainly Miss Romero-Browne must be careful, but the Countess of Deversham—surely she can do as she pleases?'

'A lady is a lady under any circumstances,' Cecy replied repressively, carving herself a slice of home-cured ham.

'Indeed?' Dominga sounded sceptical. She looked down at her plate and saw instead the faces of two handsome, arrogant young men. 'It seems to me,' she went on, 'that the higher one is up the social ladder the less one has to bother with appearances.'

'Nothing could be farther from the truth,' Cecy told her anxiously. 'I don't know where you picked up such a notion, but it will not do, my dear. And as for this belief that you will become a countess . . .'

She broke off as Dominga's brooding brown eyes settled on her and she heard her step-daughter say: 'Believing something is halfway to achieving it. One of Papa's maxims, you will remember, and when was he ever wrong?'

'But he is no longer here to arrange your marriage for you,' Cecy fretted.

Dominga reached for a fresh plate and served herself from a dish of buttered eggs. 'The matter is in hand,' she replied curtly. 'I expect to be Deversham's bride within a few weeks.'

'Sometimes I fear for you,' Cecy whispered. 'You have all your father's ambition but you forget you are a woman. I am terrified you will over-reach yourself and come to grief.'

Dominga thought of the ten golden guineas hidden in her jewel box and her eyes flashed. 'I never forget I am a woman,' she snapped. 'Not for one minute of one day. Your fears are groundless, Mama.'

Cecy was surprised by such heat and she quailed before it. 'I don't wish to vex you, Dominga, but I cannot be quite—quite comfortable about this proposed marriage. I know your revered Papa directed you to Mr Ponting, but to be managing the business yourself is—is—' Words failed her.

'Outrageous?' Dominga supplied. 'Don't fret so, because it is nothing of the kind. I have been the soul of discretion and so, too, will Mr Ponting be. I never knew a fellow so worried about his good name.'

'It's *your* good name that worries me,' Cecy, exasperated, was forced to retort.

'Eat your ham and stop nagging at me so,' Dominga advised. 'You'll only upset yourself for nothing, for you know as well as I do that no protest you might make will alter the course I have set for myself.'

Cecy, forced to acknowledge the truth of this, did as she was told and ate her breakfast, allowing herself to be placated by the approving smile Dominga bestowed upon her.

A truce, backed by a certain amount of affection, existed between them rather than a deeper, enduring relationship. Cecy had long since discovered that the way to manage Dominga was not to cross her will. For her part, Dominga knew she would be left in peace provided she committed no social solecism. Thus they contrived to live in a harmony that other, more loving, households might have envied.

When breakfast was over, Dominga said: 'I mean to walk down to the village to see the smith. Melody has a loose shoe. I'll pick up that kitten you've been promised as well, if you wish.'

'There's no need for you to exert yourself. Send a groom,' Cecy replied.

'But I wish to exert myself. I'm too restless to hang about the house all morning.'

Cecy eyed her uneasily. 'You will take Gibbons, of course?'

'As a matter of fact, no. I have given him leave to ride over to Hayleston. He had such a dull time of it in Town I thought he deserved a treat.'

'Where is the treat in visiting Hayleston?' Cecy marvelled.

'There is a cock-fight,' Dominga explained.

Cecy shuddered eloquently, then said: 'If Gibbons does not accompany you, take your maid.'

Dominga nodded with a docility that should have rung warning bells in Cecy's head, but her mind was already on her next task, which was supervising Cook in the preservation of those summer fruits which had reached the right stage of ripeness. Since this chore was very close to Cecy's heart, she was glad that Dominga would be entertaining herself this morning for, try as she might, she had never been able to arouse any housewifely instincts in her stepdaughter.

Dominga went upstairs to find Harris, her maid, awaiting her in her bed-chamber. 'I'm only walking down to the village so one of my old muslins will do,' Dominga said.

There were no 'old' clothes as such in Dominga's extensive wardrobe so Harris, a gaunt large-boned woman past her prime, rightly divined that her mistress was saving all the new gowns she had purchased on her trip to Town for more momentous occasions.

It hadn't escaped Harris's notice, either, that there were several silk gowns, utterly unsuitable for a maiden, among the crêpes and muslins. Her mistress was anticipating her marriage, of course, which wasn't to be wondered at. Rich beauties didn't languish on the marriage mart for long.

With dreams of being elevated from maid to dresser and

responsible for the appearance of a dashing young matron, who would undoubtedly take the Town by storm, Harris fetched a bronze gown of figured French muslin for Dominga's approval.

Dominga nodded briefly and allowed herself to be changed out of her riding habit and into the morning dress. She declined a parasol, telling Harris that the wide-brimmed bonnet that matched the dress would protect her complexion well enough, and then Cecy's voice was heard calling up the stairs.

'Do see what she wants, Harris,' Dominga asked, stepping over to the mirror. Not the most demure outfit, which this was, could quite conceal the intrinsic earthiness of the young lady who studied herself, and which only once had been fully exposed—on that lamentable day two years before at the inn. Dominga intended to use this quality to torment the Earl, once she was his wife, until he was as totally obsessed by her as she was by revenge.

These pleasant reflections were broken by Harris returning to the room with a basket. 'Mrs Wetherby is ailing again and your step-mama asks if you will call on her. There's a rheum potion to be delivered, and eggs, butter and cheese.'

Dominga nodded. Mrs Wetherby was the widow of Tom-coachman who had died last year, and Cecy took her duties as mistress of the Manor very seriously.

She picked up the basket and left the room, glad that Harris hadn't asked any awkward questions about who was to accompany her. Dominga had hoped she would assume it was Gibbons, as usual.

Luck was on her side when she went downstairs for there was nobody about and she was able to slip unnoticed through a side-door. She gained the orchard unobserved, and from there was able to pass through a gate into the lane that led to the village.

Though the Manor and the village were only some ten minutes' apart, the hedged lane connecting them wound this way and that, and was humped in the middle, so that the two were hidden from each other.

Dominga walked leisurely, enjoying her freedom, and allowing her mind to drift back to its main preoccupation— the Earl of Deversham. Which one would he be? The grey-eyed one who had gamed her away so lightly, or the blue-eyed one who had seduced her with the same lack of concern? Well, whichever one it was, how long would it be before she dictated her terms to him in his fine London mansion? She could not wait. She really could not wait . . .

Impatience quickened her footsteps, as if physical action could hasten the achievement of all her desires. The village, and Mrs Wetherby's house, were soon reached.

The old woman thanked Dominga for the contents of the basket and settled back to describe in harrowing fashion every ache and pain that had afflicted her over the past seventy years.

Dominga sat sedately in the little parlour, eyes mirroring sympathy and brain busy with different matters entirely. She drank a glass of elderberry wine and seized the opportunity, when offered another, to decline gracefully and make her escape.

She spent the next half-hour talking to the blacksmith, which was much more to her liking, and called at the inn for the kitten promised to her step-mama. Cecy's tom cat had not returned from its last romantic sortie and the situation at the Manor—a cosy breeding place for rats and mice— was becoming desperate.

She spent another half an hour being civil to Mrs Mellors and selecting a kitten from the litter of seven. Tucking the fluffy little black and white bundle into her basket, she bade Mrs Mellors good-bye and politely asked to be remembered to Mr Mellors, who was also in Hayleston for the cock-fight.

The buxom chambermaid Molly, the one tenuous link between Dominga and her escapade with milords Harry and Hugo, had married and moved away over a year before. Not that she had ever suspected what had truly happened that day. She'd believed, as she was told, that Dominga had changed back into her own clothes and gone home immediately when Molly had had to leave her alone.

Still, it was as well that there were no loose ends, Dominga mused, as she retraced her steps to the Manor. The possibility that the Earl would connect the lady who was Miss Romero-Browne with the pseudo-chambermaid who had been tumbled at the inn two years before, she dismissed as too remote even for conjecture.

She was approaching the hump in the lane when the kitten demonstrated its dislike of its new surroundings by leaping out of the basket and disappearing through a gap in the high hedge.

With an exclamation of annoyance, Dominga followed. She became entwined with blackberry branches growing among the hawthorn as she pushed her way through, and extricated herself at the cost of a scratch on her arm and the collapse of the heavy roll of hair pinned to the top of her head.

Her bonnet she had left in the hedge. Retrieving it, she crammed it into her basket and re-pinned her hair willy-nilly as she looked about for the kitten.

She spotted it at last and chased it through the long grass until the kitten, scenting capture, shot straight up an apple tree heavy with ripened fruit. There it settled and hissed defiant insults.

'You've chosen the wrong tree, you rascal, and you'll have to improve your language at the Manor,' Dominga told it, putting down the basket, and surveying the tree. It was old and gnarled and its branches were as conveniently placed as the rungs on a stepladder.

Dominga climbed the tree easily, the kitten retreating until it could go no higher. 'Got you,' Dominga exclaimed triumphantly. It was as she was extending her hand to grasp the kitten that she noticed her shoulder gleaming through a tear in her gown where the sleeve joined the high-waisted bodice.

She sighed and wondered what excuse she could make up for returning to the Manor looking more like a hoyden than a gently-bred young lady, then made a final lunge for the kitten. Once it was within her grasp its spitting abuse was replaced by piteous I-didn't-mean-it mewing, so that she paused to comfort it before descending.

It was her misfortune that she should be at that moment in full view of the occupants of a curricle which was going along the lane towards the Manor at a fast trot.

Only when the carriage was nearly abreast of the tree up which she perched did Dominga recognise Horace Ponting. And she gasped, the blood rushing to her face, as she realised that the reins must be in the hands of the most noble, and most hated, Earl of Deversham. The briefest glimpse of that fair hair and aristocratic cast of countenance told her that it must be so.

As if aware of being watched, Hugo glanced up. The vision of beauty he saw framed incongruously by leafy branches and rosy apples caused him to involuntarily pull up his horses. The temptation was too much for him. Beset as he was by troubles and blighted hopes, the Eve trembling among the apples was too overwhelming an invitation to slip back into his former carefree ways.

Tossing the reins to Mr Ponting with a brief command to walk the horses, he pursued the beauty through the hedge.

Mr Ponting had had a most miserable journey, knowing as he did that Miss Romero-Browne wished to meet the Earl at his London house, and imagining her emotions when he unexpectedly confronted her in her own home. Indeed, so deep in gloom had Mr Ponting sunk that the Earl had made no attempt at conversation during the past half hour. So to have the reins tossed at him with a terse command, and to see the Earl disappear through the hedge, was what he was not ready for.

'What's what? What's amiss?' Mr Ponting exclaimed.

The Earl, his curly-brimmed beaver set at a rakish angle on his fair curls and his driving coat caught tight about him as he thrust his way through the gap, said laughingly over his shoulder: 'Amiss? Why, naught but a recurrence of the original sin. And never did a sinner go to his fate more willingly. I swear I never saw a more luscious temptress.'

With that, he disappeared entirely from view, leaving a baffled Mr Ponting to goggle after him.

Dominga, seeing the Earl approach, descended the tree as rapidly as she could. But she was hampered by the kitten and she slipped and slithered as her feet groped for branches that suddenly seemed less conveniently placed than when she was ascending.

She knew she was more dishevelled than ever, and drumming through her mind were the words: He must not see me! Curse the man, he must not see me!

She could have wept with temper. How carefully she had plotted! How painstakingly she had planned their meeting.

How sweetly she had gloated over holding all the trump cards. How recurrently she had savoured watching him squirm until he humbled himself sufficiently into accepting her terms in marriage. And now this!

Herself humiliated and humbled, robbed of dignity. He would take her as a common wench, to do as he pleased with, as he had once before . . .

Oh, truly she could have wept! But he had not caught her yet, had not seen her face close up. Perhaps she could still escape him, and he none the wiser who she really was. She had but a branch or two to go when a gloved hand caught at her ankle and tugged it gently.

She gasped and clutched at the tree trunk for support, hiding her face against it. The kitten escaped and shot back to the top of the tree.

It was one of the rare moments in her life when she was totally at a loss. Just lately Mr Ponting had become very familiar with that feeling, but to Dominga it was alien and unacceptable.

She swore.

There was a shout of laughter from below her. 'What, must I pay before I touch?' Hugo exclaimed. 'Come down, my pretty, and we'll have this matter settled in a trice.'

The hand ceased tugging at her ankle. It began to caress it instead.

'Is it persuasion that is needed?' came the taunting voice. 'You shall have it, my rustic Eve. I've no business so pressing that it cannot be delayed for as long as it pleases you—and me.'

Dominga felt his hand begin to move up her leg, clad as it was in her sadly torn silk stockings. She tried to bury her face in the tree, so ashamed was she of the weakness stealing over her. That well remembered, much regretted weakness.

'How high must I go before you come down?' asked the Earl in maddeningly amused accents.

His hand lingered a little at her knee and began to stray beyond.

Dominga knew that if she was going to act it must be now, or she would be lost forever . . .

CHAPTER
EIGHT

IT was impossible to keep her face hidden any longer. She had to see him to judge how best he could be tackled. Dominga steeled herself and looked down.

She was poised for action, but what she saw momentarily paralysed her. For the eyes she was looking into were blue . . . the blue that had haunted her through two long years . . . the blue that belonged to her seducer.

So! If she had not ruined all by this day's folly, most truly could she have her revenge.

Hugo was similarly struck dumb, but not so much by the colour of her eyes, though he noted their lustrous brown depths with approval, as by her beauty as a whole. This, he thought exultantly, was the embodiment of sheer feminine perfection that a predatory male could normally only pursue in his dreams.

As his eyes lingered on her full lips, high cheekbones, ivory complexion and glossy black hair—to say nothing of the soft flesh peeping temptingly through her torn bodice—Dominga acted. She lashed out with the leg he held and her foot hit him squarely in the chest. Hugo caught off balance, staggered backwards and sprawled to the ground.

Dominga leapt from the tree and fled for the hedge while Hugo, striving to recover his wits and his feet, became entangled in his voluminous driving cape.

The language that pursued Dominga was more fit for a barrack-room than a young lady's ears, but after what she had endured thus far this day, it had no power to shake her.

It might have made Mr Ponting blush, but he heard nothing, just as he had seen nothing, for he was obeying the Earl's orders and walking the horses up and down. The chore did not please him any more than it pleased the mettlesome thoroughbreds. They were skittish and uncooperative, which only increased Mr Ponting's discomfort as he moodily contemplated the drawbacks of becoming embroiled with a short-tempered Earl and an ambitious heiress.

His misery deepened when the horses resisted being turned once more to face the Manor. He was perspiring freely by the time he had completed this fraught manoeuvre and was just beginning to relax when somebody burst through the hedge beside him, causing him to suffer such a severe spasm of shock it was a mercy he did not expire upon the spot.

The horses didn't think much of the disturbance, either, but Dominga had no time to spare for the outraged sensibilities of man or beasts as she jumped on to the driving seat and grabbed the reins.

Not recognising the elegant heiress in the tattered creature before him, Mr Ponting exclaimed indignantly: 'I say, miss! Whatever are you about? Get down this instant!'

'Let go of their heads, you dolt,' Dominga ground out. 'Haven't you the wit to know who I am?'

Mr Ponting gasped: 'Miss Romero-Browne!'

'Stand aside,' Dominga snapped. 'I must get back to the Manor before the lecher gets his hands on me again.'

'L-lecher?' Mr Ponting stuttered, feeling as if he were the only sane person in a world run well and truly mad. 'But that—that is the Earl. The man you wish to marry!'

'Stand aside,' Dominga repeated fiercely. 'Unless, of course, it is your wish to see me ravished before his ring is on my finger?'

Mr Ponting incoherently denied any such intention, then had to jump aside as the unsettled horses reared and showed every inclination to bolt.

But Dominga was no mean horsewoman and the brief battle to gain mastery of the thoroughbreds went some way towards easing her pent-up rage. As soon as she was in control again, she asked: 'Why did you bring the Earl here? It was my express wish to meet him in London.'

To be in this predicament, and then be blamed for it, was too much. Mr Ponting wrung his hands. 'I had no choice. He's as headstrong as you are. Oh, I wish I had never become involved in this!'

Since Dominga scorned anything as futile as wishful

thinking, she retorted: 'Well, you are involved. Now listen carefully. On no account tell the Earl that I am Miss Romero-Browne. He does not know me and he has no reason to suppose that you do.'

'N-not tell him? B-but when you are introduced to him at the Manor he will accuse me of p-perfidy or worse. He cannot f-fail to recognise you and he'll think we have c-conspired to m-make a fool of him.'

Dominga cast a quick glance at the hedge. What was keeping the Earl? She could not guess, but could only be grateful. She looked back at Mr Ponting, saw how honestly distressed he was and sought to strengthen him.

'Courage, my friend,' she said softly. 'There's risk in any worth-while endeavour, but we shall come about if I can gain some time in which to contrive a little. Trust me, that is all I ask.'

'T-trust you!' exclaimed the much-tried Mr Ponting. 'I can do naught else, but you misunderstand the case. It is the Earl I do not trust. He is as touchy as his horses. You do not—you cannot!—know him as I have come to.'

'Better,' Dominga told him with an enigmatic smile, 'but that is no business of yours. You may tell the Earl that I shall leave his horses tethered to a tree a short way past that hump in the lane, and that I'll not harm them. I know what I'm doing.'

With that she drove the horses forward at a smart pace, leaving Mr Ponting to find what comfort he could in her words. It was not much. He looked the most dejected man alive as he watched the curricle disappear from sight and tried to nerve himself to face the forthcoming interview with the Earl.

Indeed, what that erratic young nobleman would say when he discovered that a certain young lady had not only spurned his amorous advances but stolen his beloved horses to boot, did not bear thinking about. And what he would do when he discovered that Mr Ponting had kept quiet about her being the heiress was beyond the bounds of imagination. The muscles in Mr Ponting's legs turned to jelly. He sank on the grass verge with a moan and buried his face in his quivering hands . . .

Hugo was not feeling very well, either. By the time he

had disentangled his long legs from the cape, the wench he had lusted after had disappeared from his view.

For some moments he stayed where he was, disgusted that a seasoned campaigner like himself should have been put out of the game by anything as amateurish as a kick in the chest. He also felt a fair amount of chagrin that a wench as comely as his rustic Eve should want to resist his advances. He deeply regreted that he had not clasped her more firmly while he'd had the chance, for he was sure she would have been his if he'd managed to plant a kiss on those ripe lips. He was certain that she was a serving wench rigged up in her mistress's cast-off finery. The silk stockings on her shapely legs, for example, had seen much better days, as had the bronze gown with the intriguingly torn bodice.

All in all, she was natural prey for somebody such as himself. Perhaps he had made a tactical error in not pulling out his purse before he had attempted to pull her from the tree.

Hugo found his eyes resting on a sadly crushed bonnet reposing in a straw basket at the base of the apple tree, and then he looked higher as he heard plaintive mewing. The kitten, tiring of its adventures, had come down to the lowest branch in search once more of a human benefactor.

The Earl, ever volatile, smiled. 'Are you,' he asked aloud, 'what my lovely Eve was in search of, and not an apple after all?'

The kitten, recognising a friendly voice, mewed even more hopefully.

Hugo stood up, recovered his hat and set it upon his head, brushed down his breeches with a careless hand and then lifted the kitten from the branch. It snuggled gratefully against him.

Amused, Hugo told it: 'You give me a warmer welcome than your mistress, if that is who she is. Alas, she is not mine.'

But the smile was wiped from his face as he heard his horses galloping off. Thinking that Mr Ponting had allowed them to bolt, he put the kitten on the grass and went hastily through the gap in the hedge. He was just in time to see his curricle disappearing over the hump in the lane with the girl who had eluded him on the driving seat.

The Earl was sufficiently sporting to forgive the girl for repulsing him, but he loved his horses. The thought of them in her unskilled hands evoked the wrathful roar Mr Ponting was awaiting in no little fear and a great deal of trembling.

'What the deuce do you mean by letting that hell-born bitch steal my horses?' Hugo thundered.

Mr Ponting raised his head from his hands and replied wearily: 'I did my best, my lord, but if you could not restrain the young lady, what chance do you suppose I had?'

'Lady?' Hugo exploded. 'That hayrick harlot?'

'My lord, you might be maligning an honest maid,' Mr Ponting ventured timidly, then wished he hadn't bothered as his own character and that of Miss Romero-Browne was torn to shreds by the enraged Earl.

When he at last lapsed into fuming silence, Mr Ponting said: 'I'm sure your horses will come to no harm, my lord. She said she'd leave them tied to a tree farther along the road.'

'Did she indeed? Damned kind of her.' Hugo began to walk along the lane, adding viciously: 'It will be a mercy for her if she breaks her neck, for if she's lamed them, I swear I'll not rest until I've tracked her down.'

Mr Ponting, racking his brains to think of some way of inducing the Earl to return to London without visiting the Manor, was forced to trot to keep up with him.

'No doubt my lord is in no mood now to meet the heiress?' he asked hopefully. 'Mayhap it would be better to visit the Manor on another day?'

'My mood at this moment,' Hugo corrected him pithily, 'is to catch that wench and give her the spanking of her life. I'll teach her to meddle with my horses!'

Mr Ponting, seeing his only chance of salvation snatched from him, groaned. He trotted on, head down, convinced that his own due would be a whipping when the Earl discovered all. He considered the qualities he had endowed Miss Romero-Browne with to recommend her to the Earl, and decided he could count himself lucky if he escaped with his life.

'Trust me', the heiress had said. Well, that was exactly what he had done, and look where it had led him. Such was the look on his companion's face right now that Mr Ponting doubted very much whether the Earl would stop at murder.

It was only when they were going up the hump in the lane, and after glancing back several times, that Mr Ponting was able to rouse himself from his thoughts sufficiently to say: 'There is a kitten following us, my lord.'

'And what,' Hugo enquired icily, 'am I expected to do about it? Or am I participating in a farce?'

It appeared to have slipped his memory that their present predicament was the result of his own behaviour and, in the face of such high-bred arrogance, Mr Ponting could only lapse back into a crushed silence.

'There they are, by god,' Hugo breathed, breasting the hump and seeing that his horses were indeed tied to a tree close by. Beyond them, and set well back from the lane, he could also see the chimneys of a sizeable house which he rightly supposed was the Manor.

The Earl increased his pace, but Mr Ponting had to pause to mop his perspiring brow with a kerchief. It was a mistake, for it gave the pursuing kitten the opportunity to catch up and claw entreatingly at his best breeches.

Mr Ponting was moved to protest, but the kitten was either deaf or stupid for it only increased its assault upon his nether garments. Since the only way to stop it was to pick it up, Mr Ponting did so. Sighing, he plodded on while the kitten made itself at home in his arms, purring like a swarm of demented bumble bees.

By the time he reached the curricle, Hugo had completed an anxious inspection of his horses. 'It appears no damage has been done,' he said grudgingly, 'although I'll not rest easy until my groom has had a look at them.'

He climbed on to the driving seat, saw the kitten as Mr Ponting joined him, and went on to demand: 'What the devil have you got that thing for?'

'There was no getting rid of it. I thought I might leave it at the Manor unless—' a hopeful note crept into Mr Ponting's voice—'you have decided to postpone your visit now that your horses are unharmed?'

'Nothing could keep me from the Manor now. 'Tis my belief that plaguey wench works there and I'll find her if I have to tear the thatch from the roof. She might have ruined my horses, damn her!'

He set the team in motion at a walking pace, studying them all the while, so that he did not notice Mr Ponting's complexion change from the mottled purple induced by unaccustomed exercise to a graveyard pallor.

'My lord, consider!' he whispered. 'You cannot ask Mrs Romero-Browne to deliver up a girl you were attempting to ravish, and who saved herself as best she could.'

'Ravish?' Hugo challenged. ''Pon my soul, Ponting, I don't know what goes on in your circles, but you've got a dashed queer idea about what goes on in mine.'

'None the less, you were lusting after her,' Mr Ponting pointed out.

'Of course I was!' exploded the Earl. 'I'm a man, dammit, and what's a man expected to do when a choice morsel leads him on? Look the other way? The day I do that is the day I'm nailed into my box.'

Mr Ponting, trying to retrieve the thread of the conversation and so avert some part of the disaster awaiting him at the Manor, persisted courageously: 'Some might say, however, that you were intent on ravishing her whether she was willing or not.'

'The whole world may say it and I wouldn't care a groat. If she wasn't willing, she only had to say the word. She didn't have to steal my horses.'

'She might have been out of her mind with terror . . . didn't know what she was doing and so can't be held responsible,' Mr Ponting babbled.

'Fustian,' Hugo snarled. 'Next you'll be saying there was nothing brazen in the way she nipped off with my curricle.'

'Even so, my lord,' Mr Ponting said, finding his point again and finally making it, 'you cannot mention your—ah—adventure to a lady like Mrs Romero-Browne. It would not be seemly.'

He was right, of course, as Hugo would have already realised for himself had he not been so angry over the cavalier treatment his horses had received. It was no tale for a lady's ears. Apart from that, Hugo knew that in certain situations women, whatever their class, were inclined to stick together. A gentleman would naturally uphold that horse-stealing, under any circumstances, was reprehensible and should be punished. A lady, however, might consider these burning truths as immaterial when set beside chastity.

Hugo, turning his horses into the driveway of the Manor, knew that he must swallow his ire and hold his peace. But even so, as he drew up before the house, he said: 'You're right. We shall have to keep this between us. Not,' he added darkly, 'that I'll be responsible for my actions if I set eyes on her.'

Mr Ponting could only hope that time for reflection had shown Miss Romero-Browne the wisdom of locking herself in her bed-chamber and throwing away the key.

The sound of the carriage had brought a groom running from the stables and for some minutes the Earl was occupied in issuing stringent instructions as to the care of his team.

Only when his curricle was led away did he allow himself to study the Manor, and, eventually, to raise an eyebrow at Mr Ponting.

Rightly interpreting this as a command, Mr Ponting knocked reluctantly at the door. His last desperate hope that they would be barred entry—perhaps because some infectious disease had this moment struck down the entire household—was dashed when an unusually young but perfectly correct butler opened the door.

No sooner had Crispin learned their identity than the Earl was relieved of his cape and they were ushered into the best parlour, begged to make themselves comfortable and promised that Mrs Romero-Browne would be told immediately of their arrival.

It was not the first time that Crispin, who had only recently been elevated from first footman to butler on the untimely death of his father, had opened the door to a titled gentleman. However, this was the first time anybody as grand as a belted Earl had come his way and he was very much on his mettle.

In a matter of moments he had removed the kitten from Mr Ponting's arms, listened to the tale of its acquisition, promised to set enquiries in motion as to its owner, and bowed himself and the kitten from the room.

Hugo flung himself into an armchair and cast his eyes—

never harder to please—about him. Though the whole of Chersey Manor could be lost in one wing of Deversham Hall, and probably never found again, it was a pleasingly unpretentious residence for a family as rich as Mr Ponting had claimed. No vulgar display of wealth claimed his attention. The parlour was tastefully furnished, not in the first stare of fashion but in a style suitable for the low, beamed ceiling and the leaded windows. Only the thick carpet on the floor showed that this was an establishment where the owner could afford to indulge an expensive whim.

The Earl was surprised and wondered if Mrs Romero-Browne might prove, after all, to be the lady Mr Ponting claimed. As for the heiress herself, experience had taught him what folly it was to hope that wealth and beauty could go together.

The door opened to admit Crispin, who carried decanters, glasses and a plate of macaroons on a silver tray. Ascertaining that both visitors would like sherry, he poured for them, handed them their glasses, informed them that Mrs Romero-Browne would be with them directly, and once again bowed himself out.

Hugo sipped his sherry warily, but was surprised again. It was excellent. Someone within these walls, then, knew how a cellar should be stocked and he remarked as much to Mr Ponting.

That poor gentleman jumped at the sound of his voice, mumbled something and relapsed into stricken silence. He was sure he was only minutes away from total disaster. So awful were the scenes his mind conjured up when the Earl met Miss Romero-Browne, that he felt the thick carpet beneath his feet was only biding its time before it received his corpse.

There had been some dismay in the kitchen, too, when Crispin had carried the news of her noble visitor to Cecy, but this had been caused mostly by the fact that she was not wearing her best morning gown. Cecy had recovered quickly, however, and given her orders in a calm manner. Refreshments must be taken to the best parlour, and Miss Dominga must be found and told of the Earl's arrival. While this was being done, Cecy paused for a few moments to consider the meaning of the Earl's unexpected arrival.

The truth was that she was one of those women who were easily flustered by small events but could rise magnificently to the big occasions. And this was undoubtedly the biggest occasion that had come her way since her husband's funeral.

She knew the Earl could only be here to look Dominga over. This was a trifle puzzling, to be sure, since Dominga had said that the meeting was to be arranged in Town and that her step-mother would not be involved in the delicate matter at all, but Cecy did not allow this to throw her out of her stride.

The most immediate concern was that the household should not be found wanting in any observance to its distinguished guest. She whipped off her white apron, checked that her lace cap was not askew and sallied forth to the parlour.

Not having seen Dominga's furtive return to the Manor, she had no notion of what had occurred by the apple tree, and had been almost as surprised by Crispin carrying a kitten into the kitchen as by the news of the Earl's visit.

Her fastidious, retiring nature naturally found Dominga's machinations to ensnare the Earl repugnant, but publicly she would do her duty by lending countenance to her step-daughter's actions. A sorry mother she would be if she did not!

But what Cecy was not prepared to countenance was any aristocrat looking down his haughty nose and finding fault with her establishment. It was this determination that stiffened her spine as Crispin bowed her into the parlour, then quietly withdrew.

Cecy paused to study the two gentlemen who rose to their feet at her entrance. The chubby one in the sober clothes must be Mr Ponting, she decided, but she couldn't understand why he looked so acutely uncomfortable. She turned her attention to the other and was almost surprised into a gasp of astonishment, for it seemed as if Adonis himself had strayed into her parlour. Tall, fair and handsome, he was the living embodiment of all young maidens yearned for in their dreams before they wisely gave up all hope of ever meeting him and settled for more prosaic husbands.

This, then, was the Earl for whom Dominga craved, and Cecy could no longer wonder at it. Who would not want such a husband? And if Dominga should succeed in becoming his wife, surely the gods themselves would be jealous of such a handsome couple . . .

Cecy brought herself back from her exotic flight of fancy, moved forward with quiet dignity, held out her hand to the Earl and said pleasantly: 'I am Mrs Romero-Browne and I believe you must be the Earl of Deversham. I hope you will allow yourself to feel at home here, for you are most welcome.'

Hugo was agreeably impressed with her gentle well-bred voice. Moreover, she apparently felt no need to advertise her wealth by loading her person with diamonds during the day in the tasteless manner of so many of the *nouveaux riches*—and she displayed none of the odious toadying ways of Mrs Yerberry. Therefore, he was able to take her hand and bow over it with exactly the right degree of nicety.

Cecy bestowed on him a smile which he found singularly sweet, then looked at his companion. 'You, sir, are Mr Ponting?' she asked. 'How do you do. My step-daughter will be joining us shortly.'

Mr Ponting bowed deeply over her hand and uttered a series of disjointed sentences which reinforced her original impression of his being extremely nervous.

Cecy invited him and the Earl to sit down, did so herself, and engaged them both in polite conversation. She further charmed Hugo by making no sly references as to the cause of his visit, and proved that even if she was not accustomed to moving in the first circles, she was at ease in distinguished company.

Hugo played his part in the conversation but not one word could be wrung from Mr Ponting. Seeing how frequently he fidgeted in his chair, Cecy was at last moved to ask kindly: 'Pray, sir, is anything amiss?'

Mr Ponting started up in his chair as if he had been shot. 'No! No! Nothing,' he denied. As this brought the Earl's as well as his hostess's eyes upon him, he hastened to add: 'That is . . . thinking about milord's horses. They had a—a—hard journey, you see. Thoroughbreds, you know. Easily upset. They—' Realising he could make no refer-

ence to the way Miss Dominga Romero-Browne had com-
mandeered them, his voice trailed away miserably.

Cecy's eyebrows rose and she looked at the Earl. 'You
can trust my groom, my lord. He is used to looking after
blood-cattle. If you will feel easier in your mind, however, I
will accompany you to the stables. I know how gentlemen
can be about their horses! Not only gentlemen, either. My
step-daughter seems to be forever fretting over loose shoes
and spavins, and goodness knows what, as she would tell
you if she were here.'

As if on cue, the door opened and Dominga entered.
Cecy looked at her and smiled with approval. She was not
to know, of course, that the maid Harris had earned her
yearly stipend in a few short minutes by transforming a
disgraceful hoyden into a young lady whose appearance and apparel were beyond reproach. Harris had
neither nagged nor reproached Dominga as she had set
about this task. The information hastily imparted to her
that the Earl of Deversham was about to call had turned
them from maid and mistress to two women with a common cause.

Dominga was stripped and washed, and the tangles were
so ruthlessly brushed from her hair that tears would have
spilled from her eyes had she been any less resolute than
her maid.

While Dominga put on new silk stockings, Harris snatched from the wardrobe exactly the right gown for the
occasion. It was grey, which was suitable for Dominga's
semi-mourning state, and its apparent modesty was fitting
for a young lady who had only just emerged from the
schoolroom. But on Dominga the tight, high-necked
bodice could not help but emphasise her full breasts, and
the long sleeves concealed the scratches on her arms which
had been caused by the brambles in the hedge.

A tiny row of mother-of-pearl buttons stitched from the
neck to where the skirt met the high-waisted bodice was its
only decoration. A less striking girl might have bewailed
the gown's lack of frills and ribbons, but Dominga had the
good sense to know that she had no need for fussy details.
Grey silk slippers with dainty heels, a grey reticule and tiny
pearl ear-rings completed her appearance, so it was small

wonder that Cecy should look on her with such approval as she entered the parlour.

As for Dominga, she held her back straight and her head high for she had no idea what the Earl's reaction to her would be. All she could do was depend on his breeding as a gentleman to conceal from her step-mama the circumstances in which he had found her some half hour ago.

She glanced fleetingly at Mr Ponting as he rose on tottering legs and bowed, an action that was akin to a condemned man who had no choice but to put his head upon the block.

Hugo, too, had risen to his feet and as Dominga turned towards him recognition was instant. She held his eyes challengingly as his blazed like blue fire.

It was fortunate Cecy was looking at her step-daughter, for only Dominga saw Hugo's jaw clench as he suppressed the oath that rose to his lips. Mr Ponting's head was still bowed, his eyes studying the carpet as if its pattern would reveal the secret of his salvation.

Fury and chagrin flickered across Hugo's handsome face and his fists clenched involuntarily, but he was a victim of common civility. He could not cause a scene in his hostess's parlour, much as he wanted to hurl the young lady looking at him so coolly across his knee and give her the spanking of her life.

Cecy, the only one in the room unaware of any seething undercurrents of emotion, went over to Dominga and took her arm. She led her towards Hugo, saying: 'You are acquainted with Mr Ponting, my dear, but let me present you to the Earl of Deversham.'

Dominga stood in front of the Earl, curtsied prettily and extended her hand to him. Hugo touched her fingers briefly and gave her so slight a bow that Cecy would have been puzzled had she not seen many men so overcome by her step-daughter's beauty that they had forgotten the social graces.

She had no reason to suppose that the Earl would be any less stricken and so she smiled fondly on the pair, thinking that few could have had the honour of bringing two such splendid creatures together. It was only when she noticed that she was the only person in the parlour who was not frozen into immobility that she wondered if anything could be amiss.

Mr Ponting, having at last gathered the courage to raise his eyes, was staring at the young couple for all the world like one who had been stuffed, an impression that was heightened by the look of horror in his eyes.

Bewildered, Cecy glanced at the Earl and saw that his eyes had iced into blue diamonds, while Dominga's chin was lifted in a decidedly militant manner.

Poor Cecy was at a loss, and asked: 'Pray, is anything the matter?'

No one moved or said anything. No one appeared even to have heard her. Not so much as a half-stuttered word came from Mr Ponting, and Dominga and the Earl went on staring at each other with anything but the light of love in their eyes.

For some undetermined reason, Cecy felt close to swooning, but it was Mr Ponting who sank senseless to the floor.

CHAPTER
NINE

ALTHOUGH Mr Ponting was not in any condition to be aware of it, he did Dominga a great service by swooning away so dramatically, for he drew the Earl's attention away from her, and thus released the tension from the atmosphere.

Not that Hugo was appreciative. 'Oh, my god, what next?' he exclaimed. 'When do they bring on the dancing bears?'

A low chuckle broke involuntarily from Dominga who, with great dramatic capabilities of her own, thought that Mr Ponting had staged this timely interruption to her formal presentation to the Earl. Only when Hugo proved himself a man of strength as well as a man of action by lifting the portly man of business from the floor and depositing him unceremoniously on a sofa did she see from Mr Ponting's ashen face that he was not play acting.

Cecy, clucking and tutting her concern, bustled over to minister to her stricken guest. It was as well that Mr Ponting had no pretensions to fashion for his neckcloth was a sorry sight when she had finished loosening it.

'The poor man,' she murmured. 'The drive from London in this heat must have been too much for him.' Then, remembering the fraught atmosphere in the room before Mr Ponting had been overcome, she looked up uncertainly at Dominga. 'Unless, my dear, you can think of anything else that might have distressed him?'

'I can,' Hugo broke in curtly, recalling the creaks that accompanied any unguarded movement Mr Ponting made. 'I'll lay a monkey to a groat he's laced up tighter than a drum.' Catching sight of Cecy's baffled expression, he added apologetically: 'A corset, ma'am, if you'll forgive my bluntness. He'll come round fast enough once the—er—article is loosened or removed.'

Cecy looked relieved rather than dismayed at this piece

of intelligence, and summoned Crispin and a footman to remove Mr Ponting to a bedchamber.

This did not take long as various servants had apparently found tasks which urgently needed carrying out in the hall, so keen were they to catch a glimpse of the Earl who, rumour had it, had come courting Miss Dominga.

'He shall have my own vinaigrette and I shall myself prepare a reviving draught of sal volatile,' Cecy said, preparing to follow as Mr Ponting was carried from the room. Then she paused and her black silk dress rustled agitatedly as she looked from the Earl to Dominga. It had just occurred to her that it would be improper to leave them unchaperoned, and yet there was no doubt that Mr Ponting had a greater claim upon her services at this moment.

Dominga, ever the opportunist, came readily to her rescue. 'The Earl and I could take a turn about the garden until you are free to rejoin us, Mama. I collect there can be no objection to that?'

Cecy seized eagerly on this solution to her difficulties, for not even a high-stickler could find anything compromising in a young couple walking in full view of anybody who might be interested. 'That would be just the thing!' She turned to the Earl and added: 'Provided, of course, that you are agreeable, my lord?'

Hugo, wanting nothing more than a few minutes alone with Dominga, replied: 'Certainly, ma'am. Don't bother your head about us for I'm sure we shall find plenty to talk about.'

Vague anxiety stirred again in Cecy's breast, but since she could see nothing in the Earl's demeanour to account for it, she said: 'We have no formal gardens here, but you'll find the orchard cool and pleasing. I'm sorry to leave you in this way, but I must admit I am anxious about Mr Ponting. Servants are all very well, but they cannot be depended upon in a case such as this unless they are closely supervised.'

They all left the room together and found Harris hovering in the hall with a grey parasol, since she had learned from a shamelessly eavesdropping servant that her mistress was about to go out walking.

Harris was not a romantic. Having suffered a severe

disappointment while still being young and foolish enough to trust a man, she had come to regard men as a necessary evil and no more. Unlike the other servants, who fondly imagined they were witnessing a romance straight out of the covers of a novel, she wished to see the Earl merely to assess her mistress's chances of winning him. She was displeased when she saw how young and fair and handsome he was, because this meant he could afford to be choosey, even had he not been a nobleman. He was the type who left broken hearts wherever he went, for the world was full of women with more eyes than brains, and as a husband he would undoubtedly be a handful.

But so was her mistress, and Harris was sure that no man could hold out for long against her charms. The maid had no chance to observe more for, as she dropped a curtsy and handed over the parasol, her mistress and the Earl walked on and out of the house.

Harris stood there, reflecting that Miss Dominga would have plenty of opportunity to use her womanly wiles while she was alone with the Earl, when Cecy called to her to lend a hand with the other guest, the unimportant one, who had been carried upstairs.

The truth, had Harris but known it, was that the Earl had never looked farther from a state of enchantment than when he crossed the cobbled yard with Dominga. No words could describe how he had felt when the thieving hoyden he had itched to spank had been formally presented to him as the heiress aspiring to share his name. The words were forming readily enough now, however, and he was merely biding his time until they were far enough from the house for them to be uttered.

His fury smouldered anew as he recalled the brass-faced way she had curtsied before him in the parlour, all composure and seeming innocence, as if she had not previously enticed him and then driven off with his curricle.

To think, also, that Ponting had recommended her as a female of delicacy. Delicacy! What a fine joke that would have been, Hugo fumed, had it been played on anybody but himself. Well, there would be a reckoning with Ponting—as that gentleman knew all too well if the way he had swooned was any guide. If the female beside him had succumbed to such a display of sensibility, he might—might!—have softened towards her. But had she? Oh, no! She had given him back stare for stare, as cool as you please, which could only confirm that she was more suited to the role of Jezebel than countess.

He cast a fulminating glance at her. She looked the very epitome of untroubled innocence as she walked beside him, parasol held primly against the strong rays of the sun. He could only wonder at her nerve in daring to be alone with him after all that had gone before, but then, what did he know of Cit's daughters? And what did she know of noblemen if she smugly imagined that the danger she stood in from him had passed?

Dominga, in fact, had a very lively awareness of the precariousness of her position, for she sensed the Earl's rage as if it were a live thing flickering between them. But she had to dare all to win all, and it was excitement rather than fear which thrilled her as she prepared to battle through to success even though the game had gone against her.

She must have this man, she really must, for she would never know peace unless she carried out her plan to the full. Indeed, her experiences with him this day had made her more determined than ever to teach him that Miss Dominga Romero-Browne was no plaything to be trifled with and tossed aside, but a lifelong commitment he could not escape.

None of this heady emotion was revealed by her expression as she paused for the Earl to open the weathered wooden gate which gave access to the orchard. She ignored the irony in his bow as he stood back for her to pass through, but she could not help thinking that the click with which he closed the gate behind them had an air of finality about it.

She had the feeling that they might have been the only people in the world, save that they were no Adam and Eve come to frolic beneath the fruit-laden trees. Indeed, the thought forcibly crossed her mind as they turned face to face that they were more like gladiators about to test each other's strengths and weaknesses in some rustic latter-day arena.

'So, miss, we are alone at last,' was Hugo's opening thrust. 'If you were a man I'd thrash you to within an inch of your life for daring to touch my horses.'

'If I were a man I would have had no need of your horses for my virtue would not have been in danger,' Dominga pointed out calmly.

'Virtue!' Hugo scoffed. 'You're a curst cool customer. What virtue is there in a female who exposes her limbs for the delectation of any passer-by?'

'Pray save your epithets for more fitting company. My head is still ringing with those I had to endure from you not an hour since. I—'

But Hugo broke in: 'I'll never find more fitting company than yours, miss. Don't think I can be beguiled by these airs and graces you affect now. I know you for what you are.'

'You know nothing of me,' Dominga replied, and was pleased with the throbbing outrage she infused in her voice. 'You choose to believe certain things, that is all, to soothe your vanity and your—your thwarted desire.'

She turned her face away from his at these last words and began to walk, as if overcome by maidenly modesty at being forced to mention anything as base as desire. She wished she could raise a blush to support her pose, but that was beyond even her histrionic talent.

'Let me reassure you on one point, miss,' Hugo said heatedly, striding after her. 'Any desire I might have felt for you died when you stole my horses. Good god, a wench who would do that goes beyond the bounds of anything I'd allow.'

'I did not steal your horses. I merely borrowed them to escape you. Can you not feel for me, my lord, in the predicament I found myself in? My only crime was rashness in trying to rescue a kitten from a tree, but the field was deserted and the lane is used most infrequently. Had I known—had I dreamed—that you would come along . . .'

'Very pretty, miss,' Hugo observed cynically, 'but I am not green enough to be taken in by any tale of yours. Where, if you are the lady you pretend to be, was your maid? Or your groom? Young ladies of my acquaintance do not frolic alone in fields.'

Dominga hung her head. 'I confess it was indiscreet of

me to walk out alone, but the blame for all the rest lies at
your door, not mine.'

'Oh, does it?' Hugo answered. 'But what maiden of true
modesty would, some half-hour after being accosted by an
unknown man, allow herself to be presented to him as if
nothing untoward had happened?'

'I was trying to save my step-mama from distress,'
Dominga murmured. 'Poor Cecy would have been horrified had she heard of my—my—adventure, and would
have blamed herself for not taking proper care of me. I
sought to spare her from that, for it would have been most
unfair.'

Hugo was silent as he absorbed this and Dominga,
sensing that he was wavering between belief and disbelief,
dared to smile at him a little. 'If I am to be wholly truthful,'
she confessed, 'my motives for holding my tongue over
what had occurred were not entirely noble. I also wished to
save myself from a scold.'

She looked and sounded charmingly honest, and yet
Hugo could not quite rid himself of the feeling that he was
being hoodwinked. He had a very highly developed instinct
for self-survival which was sending out strong enough
signals to quite negate the very different signals being sent
out by Dominga's brown eyes, large and lustrous though
they were as they gazed into his own.

Besides, there was no denying that his true taste in
women favoured blondes. Fair, fragile creatures who tan-
talised a man into searching for the fire beneath the ice.
Heady, ripe brunettes such as this strangely-named
Dominga Romero-Browne were all right for a hasty tumble, but they lacked the mystery that could chain a man for
life. So thought Hugo, tormented again by a vision of the
incomparable Désirée. That priggish bore Marsham would
have the joy of her while he . . . he . . .

Dominga, surprised and miffed to find that his attention
had wandered from her, said persuasively: 'The real rub is
that I took your horses, is it not? Yet you have seen for
yourself, my lord, that they came to no harm at my hands.
The incident was regrettable, certainly, but not disastrous,
so could we not forget about it?'

But Hugo, blinking the image of Désirée from his eyes

and focusing again on Dominga, was not yet ready to listen to the sweet voice of reason. 'Why didn't Ponting tell me he knew you? There's something dashed havey-cavey going on here and I'm not a man who cares to be duped.'

Dominga did not answer immediately because she was crossing a plank which spanned a little brook running through the orchard, and she was minding her balance. When she reached the other side safely, she said: 'Poor Mr Ponting could do naught else. He is in my employ and I ordered him to hold his tongue. I needed time in which to correct the false impression you had gained of me.'

Hugo, scorning the plank and leaping the brook, thought that she was a very smooth talker—and persuasive. And yet something . . . something about her worried him. Every so often she seemed to strike some chord in his mind, some memory, which, strive as he could, evaded him.

It was irritating and prompted him to ask suddenly: 'Have we met before?'

Panic gripped Dominga. No sooner did she vanquish one spectre which loomed between her and her coronet than another raised itself. 'Had our paths crossed I'm sure I would have remembered you, but I have lived in seclusion here all my life. As you might well imagine, distinguished visitors are rare in such rural parts as this.'

'H'm,' Hugo said non-committally, then was silent. He knew that but for the earlier encounter by the apple tree he would have been favourably impressed with Miss Romero-Browne.

Her husky voice pleased his ear and, prejudiced against her as he was now, he still had to admit she was a feast for a man's eyes. Moreover, she dressed well and walked well. There was not a thing about her, in fact, which pointed to vulgar parentage, and she was very rich.

He could not put his finger on whatever it was about her that troubled him, but it held him back from committing himself. Yet he had to settle for Isabelle or Dominga and, of the two, only a madman would favour Isabelle. So why did he not propose and get it over with? Hugo could only conclude that he lacked Désirée's facility for grasping the right straw when it was offered, and prepared to force himself.

Dominga had reached a bench shaded by a cherry tree. She closed her parasol and sat down. She looked up at the rich clusters of cherries above her head and observed: 'Did you know, my lord, that a good cherry crop such as this is held to be a sign of good fortune?'

'I did not,' Hugo returned shortly, his mind on other things. 'Stand up, miss. I wish to look at you.'

Now a flush did stain Dominga's cheeks, the slow deep red that was a warning to the initiated that a rage was beginning to burn within her. The look she gave the Earl was quite as haughty as his own for he was doing it again—treating her as if she were of no account.

'Come now,' he went on irritably. 'If you put yourself in the market place you can't cavil at having the goods looked over.'

Dominga's hands clenched into fists. She opened her mouth to dispute who was buying and who was selling here, then smothered the words. Hugo was within her grasp if only she could keep her temper, and then there would be a whole lifetime in which to salvage her pride at the expense of his.

She forced herself to relax and rose gracefully to her feet. But she was mortified anew when he took a pace or two backwards to survey her, then calmly asked her to turn around.

'My lord, you go too far,' she said through gritted teeth. 'I am a woman not a horse.'

'Which is as well,' Hugo replied, 'since a horse would have to undergo a far more thorough examination before it was admitted to my stables. But then, I've seen enough of your limbs to be sure they are shapely enough.'

Dominga gasped, and she was not acting. 'How dare you! I cannot believe a gentleman would speak to me in such a way.'

But Hugo hated this business of selecting an heiress, and it made him hateful. 'Gentleman?' he questioned insolently. 'What the deuce has that to do with me? I am a nobleman.'

'I thought, my lord, that the two were inseparable,' she snapped, her voice huskier than ever with anger, hard though she fought to master it.

'Which just shows, Miss Romero-Browne, how very much you have to learn.'

'And you must learn that an heiress with a dowry of fifty thousand pounds expects at least civility from a suitor,' Dominga told him roundly.

'You over-reach yourself,' Hugo pointed out silkily. 'My case is not so desperate that I must settle for *any* moneyed female, nor do I have to exert myself to catch their interest. When it comes to a title such as mine, heiresses need precious little encouragement.'

Dominga took a deep breath. 'Had you not been interested in me, you would never have come here.'

'More curiosity than interest, miss. How can one pick a winner unless one surveys all the runners in the race?'

'I know the "runners" better than you do yourself,' Dominga replied, almost spitting out the word that offended her, and the truth rang in her voice because her father had left her a detailed list of all females who might set themselves up in opposition to her plans. 'Certainly there is no more to be said if you desire a wife who squints, or has spots, or a beak of a nose, or undesirable relatives. Take your pick among them and breed similarly unattractive children if this is your desire. But as for myself, I have no such impediments and a great deal more money to boot.'

'I wonder why the underbred always use money as a yardstick for everything?' Hugo mused, to Dominga's chagrin. 'However, since one must contrive to adapt oneself to present company, I'll take leave to tell you that fifty thousand pounds will not purchase my name.'

Dominga digested this in silence for some moments, then asked: 'How much?'

'As I told Mr Ponting, half of your principal and all of your yearly income. He rather thought that your father's Will forbade it, but that the matter could be debated.' Hugo gave her a look of insufferable disdain, then went on: 'Truth to tell, I'm in no mood for bargaining. That's something more suited to lawyers—or Cits.'

Dominga was so staggered by his demand that for once his insolence missed its mark. The price was too high, even for her revenge, and yet she thought she knew his weak spots now and could out-manoeuvre him. 'A dowry is so commonplace it is not worth remarking on, but if you held out for my yearly income would not that make you my pensioner? I would have thought, short though our acquaintance has been, that you were too proud for that.'

Hugo was the one thunderstruck now. Curse her impudence, and curse her doubly for being right! But he had no chance to say anything for she was going on smoothly: 'I understand how bitter you must be about your debts, for they are inherited and none of your making, but extending that bitterness towards me seems most unfair.'

She paused to allow her words to sink in, then continued: 'Your estates, put right and properly managed, will produce within a few years an income to rival my own. Thus you would be, as I'm sure your pride would wish, fully independent of me financially. Do I read the case correctly, my lord?'

She did, but Hugo was irked that she could be so rational while he was swayed this way and that by his emotions.

When he failed to answer, Dominga asked calmly: 'What if my dowry were a hundred thousand pounds? Would not that allow you to redeem your debts and also put your lands in order? If so, you will have achieved your ends with no slight to your pride since, as I have said, a bride is expected to have a dowry.'

Dominga held her breath as she waited for his answer. She had put the sting in, then administered the salve, and though she didn't hope for gratitude she had some right to expect that he would be more reasonable.

But Hugo only went off on a tangent by demanding: 'Why me?'

'Just as you must settle for the best on offer, so must I,' she returned equably. 'If I had a taste for a Royal duke and a morganatic marriage the case might be different but—' Dominga wrinkled her nose fastidiously—'such is not the case.'

'Great heavens, you value yourself highly,' Hugo breathed.

She raised her eyebrows. 'With reason, surely? As do you, I believe?'

Hugo's lip curled. 'Too damned highly to become entangled with you.'

'You are allowing your pride to master your reason, my lord,' Dominga chided him. 'Your first objective is saving your estates. My dowry will ensure that. Your second is selecting a wife fit to be a countess, and I have been reared all my life to fill such a position. Your third objective must be to get the business over with quickly and neatly, and I'll not hold out for a Society wedding. So, pray, where can your objection to me lie?'

'You're too damn dictatorial for my taste. I'll have no petticoat government in my house.'

'As to that, I'll engage not to interfere unreasonably with your life, as I shall expect you not to interfere with mine,' Dominga promised.

'Then you expect too much!' Hugo exclaimed. 'If you think a wedding ring will give you the right to behave as you please, then that's the end of it. I'll have no back-door bastards masquerading under my name.'

'This is plain talking, indeed, but I would scarcely spend a fortune on becoming a countess unless I intended to keep the line legitimate,' Dominga retorted. 'I will do my duty but, after that, I'm sure you will not wish me to be forever hanging on your arm.'

There was truth in that, and Hugo saw at once the advantage of having a complaisant countess. It would make it easier for him to pursue his *affaire* with Désirée, for whom his very bones seemed to ache. Not that Isabelle Yerberry would have the spirit to fight such a rival, but her mother could be depended on to make the deuce of a fuss. So what was it to be? Ditch Isabelle, marry this Cit's daughter and romance with Désirée on the side? Ultimately he would be able to fulfil all his desires, both for his lands and his lady love.

'I suppose it must be done,' Hugo muttered, 'but god only knows how much it cuts into me to allow a tradesman's daughter through the front door.'

He did not realise he had spoken aloud, but his words reached Dominga and her spine stiffened. She sought for a way to wound him, as he so carelessly kept wounding her, and after a second or two she found it. None knew better than she how lusty Hugo was, and to deny herself to him would surely torment him as he had never been tormented before. What a piquant situation it would be for him to have a desirable wife and be unable to touch her.

She said dulcetly: 'One condition only would I lay upon our marriage contract, my lord, and that is that my bed-chamber should be my own for a year. I wish to establish myself securely in Society before I find myself—' she cast down her eyes modestly—'in an interesting condition. Since I will have invested so much money in achieving this ambition, I am sure you will not find this request unreasonable.'

Hugo found it more than unreasonable, he found it outrageous. Nothing could have been more calculated to scorch his manly pride in his bedroom prowess than to be rejected as a lover by the woman who was going to be his wife!

He said with an insolence designed to flay Dominga in her turn: 'Gad, miss, I'm sure a promise was never more readily given. It will take me all of a year to overcome my abhorrence of handling a Cit's daughter.'

Two bright spots of colour burned in Dominga's cheeks. Never had war been more plainly declared, but she would not be the one who retreated in confusion. She would drive him mad with desire until he broke his promise, and thus shamed himself, while she could enjoy the interesting spectacle of having an aristocrat grovelling at her feet.

'What a triumph that would be!

'You say nothing, miss,' Hugo murmured. 'Mayhap this marriage is not to your liking, after all?'

'I was just reflecting on what you said earlier about a gentleman and a nobleman not necessarily being one and the same thing,' Dominga replied. 'What guarantee have I that your promise will be kept?'

'You can trust my word,' Hugo flung at her, his temper soaring again. 'My word, and nothing else. 'Struth, you must dearly wish to be a countess to stomach the insults I have given you and yet come back for more. Does not your courage fail you? There's still time to cast your net around some tamer aristocrat.'

'I think we will deal well enough together,' Dominga told him. 'It frets you to find yourself in need of a rich wife, and it is awkward for me to have to manage the business myself because of my father's untimely death earlier this year. It is natural enough, I suppose, that under these circumstances we should chafe each other, but I'm sure all will be well when we are more accustomed to the situation.'

Hugo frowned over this, then asked: 'Would you marry any earl, or did your father pick me in particular?'

'My father wished me to marry into an ancient and illustrious house but, since he was fond of me, he desired also that my husband should be young and not unattractive. The Earl of Deversham seemed exactly right.' She had to go on to say, before he did: 'The Earl at that time was your brother.'

'Damn Harry and his reckless ways. He never did me a worse turn than when he broke his neck!' Hugo exclaimed, not for the first time.

'As to that, I am no judge,' Dominga said demurely. 'I only know I was a dutiful daughter and I will strive to become a dutiful wife.'

'You'll not be a proper wife at all for a year,' Hugo snapped, then could have kicked himself for mentioning his still-simmering grievance.

'But I shall be a countess and that will suffice. I know it is all vanity to wish to be a leading light in Society, but it would be wrong of me to pretend I am perfect. Besides which,' she added shrewdly, 'I should think a paragon would be rather uncomfortable to live with, and I shall strive to make you very comfortable.'

'But not warm my bed?' Hugo was unable to leave the subject alone.

Dominga raised her large brown eyes, all softness now, to his hard blue ones. 'A year is not so very long,' she murmured, and sought to dazzle him with her most radiant smile.

It was a mistake. Hugo, getting the full impact of her dimpled cheeks and dancing eyes, received also a blinding revelation. He took a step back from her and swore: 'Good god, I have it now—that thing about you that has nagged at me. Some two or three years back when I was on furlough from the army, my brother and I stayed in an inn in this vicinity. There was a chambermaid—a most lusty and obliging chambermaid . . .'

Hugo grasped Dominga by the arms, pulled her to him and then shook her. 'You, miss! You were the chamber-maid!'

CHAPTER
TEN

DOMINGA averted her head as if too mortified to face him and said beseechingly: 'Pray do not shake me so, my lord. You mistake the matter and thereby do me great wrong. The person you encountered is one I can scarcely be expected to recognise, nor even speak of. But the truth, since you are determined to have it, is that she is a by-blow of my father's who, thankfully, has now married and moved north. It was not kind of you to remind me of her, but you were not to know.'

Having thus craftily exonerated herself and him, Dominga continued to give the impression of striving to recover her composure after being thrown into confusion by his accusation and assault.

Hugo's response to her plea was to release her so abruptly that she fell back upon the bench, but his silence was so prolonged that she was uneasy. She added imploringly: 'I must beg you never to mention her to me again. It would be most—most unchivalrous.'

Hugo appreciated readily enough that it would be more than unchivalrous, it would be against the code of conduct by which he lived. Gentlemen were expected to acknowledge their bastards to the extent of making some settlement upon their mothers, but ladies were supposed to know nothing of such matters.

He reflected bad-temperedly that he had committed a social solecism by jumping to a conclusion which a moment's reflection would have shown him must be wrong. An heiress would never have masqueraded as a common serving wench in order to make herself available for any passing buck's pleasure, and no doubt he had imagined the two were more alike than they actually were. There had been many women in his life since that chambermaid, and although he retained a fond memory or two of her he could not be expected to remember everything.

Hugo was rattled, though, that he had put himself into a position where he had to beg Miss Romero-Browne's pardon and it was with some stiffness that he said: 'I owe you an apology. Please accept it along with my assurance that the matter I referred to will be erased from my memory.'

What a pompous ass I sound, Hugo thought disgustedly, but he was not out of the woods yet. There was something else, just as unpalatable, which had to be said. Finding that the heiress had recovered sufficiently to raise her eyes to his, he went on: 'If my lawyers find that the documents Mr Ponting has given into my care are in every detail correct, you may consider us betrothed. Since we've been very frank, I won't profess to regard our marriage as anything other than a necessary evil, so don't expect me to make a cake of myself by pretending any affection I don't feel.'

It must have been the most ungracious proposal of all time, but it was sheer enchantment to Dominga. She would have picked no fault with whatever words he had used. There had already been too many times during this interview when her coronet would have slipped for ever from her grasp but for her tenacity and guile. She knew that she must take no more risks until she was his bride.

As for Hugo, once his ramshackle proposal was delivered he showed no inclination to linger with his future wife. 'I suggest we return to the house, miss,' he told her. 'Mr Ponting has had time to recover from a dozen swoons by now.'

Dominga stood up willingly enough, but as she put up her parasol and fell into step beside him, she said: 'You really must bring yourself to use my name. In our new circumstances you cannot keep calling me "miss".'

Hugo bowed slightly but strolled on without saying anything, so Dominga was free to pursue her own thoughts. She considered it a pity that Hugo had not fallen in love with her at first sight, as so many gentlemen were wont to do, but there was no fooling herself on that head. Her seduction by the Earl two years ago had ensured that she would never again confuse lust with love.

So, with Hugo palpably proof against her charms, she knew that if his lawyers discovered the truth about her mother she would never be his bride. Proud as he was, he'd have to be besotted to the point of lunacy not to recoil from marrying a gipsy's daughter.

Dominga then allowed herself a few moments in which to puzzle why, when Hugo's blood was so hot, his heart was so hard. The obvious solution, that another woman had a prior claim upon his affections, was not long occurring to her and she frowned. If that was the case, then that woman must be vanquished along with any other obstacle between herself and her revenge.

Hugo observed her change of expression and said: 'You look as little pleased with this day's work as I am. What bothers you? Is there something you have held back about yourself that I should know?'

Dominga looked up at his handsome face, every feature of which was etched eternally upon her memory. His fair hair, his strong chin, his aristocratic nose, his firm lips and, of course, his blue, blue eyes. There could be no other man so easy to love, she thought, if one didn't know enough about him to hate him instead.

'Well?' Hugo prompted her. 'What is it?'

'Why, nothing, my lord. What could I have held back? If anything, I have been over-frank with you. I fear that if you are looking for some mystery, then you will be disappointed.'

Thwarted, Hugo tried another line of questioning. 'What will your step-mother do when you marry?'

'Remain here at the Manor, where she is happiest,' responded Dominga, thinking how refreshing it was to tell the truth occasionally although she revelled in the duplicity which came naturally to her. 'Have no fear, my lord. You marry me, not a family.'

But their private conversation was at an end for as they came through the last of the trees in the orchard they saw Mr Ponting and Cecy coming towards them.

Mr Ponting, having had his corset loosened by Crispin, had recovered consciousness to find Cecy by his bedside with a reviving cordial. He had swallowed it dutifully, though thinking that a hefty tot of brandy was what he really stood in need of. His colour had returned, however, and his apologies for so inconveniencing his hostess were profuse, but no sooner had he learned that the Earl and Miss Romero-Browne were walking alone outside the house than he had almost fainted away again.

He'd feared for her skin as well as his own and became so ashen that Cecy insisted he should rest longer upon the bed. Such was his agitation, though, that after some argument Cecy allowed him to leave the bedchamber and walk with her to find the young couple.

Nothing could have exceeded Mr Ponting's relief when he saw that his client was not only unscathed but looking as self-possessed as ever, and he could only assume her loveliness had worked its magic. He looked next to the Earl, his eyes full of the humble uncertainty of a dog who knows not whether it will get a pat or a whipping.

There was a certain tight-lipped impassiveness about the Earl's expression which did not encourage Mr Ponting to think that all was well yet, but neither did he appear to be in one of his towering passions.

As Mr Ponting opened the orchard gate for the Earl and Dominga to pass through, he racked his brains for some harmless topic of conversation he could introduce. No such safe subject materialised, so he was grateful when Cecy spared him the necessity of uttering anything by saying to his lordship: 'I am sure you will be as relieved as myself to see that Mr Ponting has made a good recovery. A light luncheon, I am persuaded, is all he needs to set him up for the return journey, if it would please your lordship to join us.'

Hugo's bow disguised the fact that it didn't please him at all to remain at the Manor, but to drive his horses back to London before they were fully rested was out of the question. However desperate his straits, he was a man who always kept his priorities right. It would be better to endure another hour or two of the heiress's company than have his horses knocked up.

Cecy began to walk with him to the house, but Dominga lingered behind while Mr Ponting closed the gate and restrained him with a hand upon his arm until Cecy and Hugo were out of earshot.

Not that Mr Ponting needed restraining, for there was much he had to say to her. 'I cannot tell you, Miss Romero-Browne, what my feelings were when I recovered my senses to discover you were alone with the Earl,' he began. 'He was in a most fearsome mood and had—had—threatened violence towards your person.'

But Dominga only laughed. 'Did I not tell you to trust me? The Earl, far from offering me violence, offered instead for my hand in marriage.'

Joy, doubt and incredulity fought to master Mr Ponting's voice as he exclaimed: 'This is beyond anything! You have not made a mistake?'

Dominga twirled her parasol gaily. 'Mistake whether or not I am to be a countess? I'd find it easier to mistake my own name. You and I have naught to do except leave the lawyers to bicker over the details.'

Mr Ponting could not be quite so sanguine. 'They will bicker, too, if I know lawyers, so we must not consider ourselves safely home yet.'

'My lawyers have orders to speed the matter through, and the Earl's financial position will ensure that his lawyers do not drag their feet, either,' Dominga replied confidently as she started to walk after Hugo and Cecy, who were almost at the house.

'There are things you do not know,' Mr Ponting fretted, then jumped as Dominga swung round on him.

'What things?' she demanded.

''Pon my soul, Miss Romero-Browne,' he expostulated, 'your moods veer as sharply as the Earl's, and it's most upsetting. Half the time I know not whether I'm on my head or my heels.'

'Forgive me,' Dominga said, feeling she would never learn what he had to say unless she soothed him. 'I know you have had an uncomfortable time of it, but that is over now. You are already one hundred guineas in credit, with the real money yet to come, so tell me what it is I should know.'

Nobody, thought Mr Ponting in some exasperation, could be more charming than Miss Romero-Browne when she chose, but the alarming feeling was growing on him that her reassuring smiles were as little to be trusted as a dentist's before a tooth was drawn. It wasn't fair, he grumbled to himself, that some should be so rich that others had to risk life and limb to earn a few crumbs dropped from their tables. Not, he mused on a trifle more cheerfully, that five hundred guineas could quite be described as crumbs. Not in his world, at any rate.

'Your news, Mr Ponting,' Dominga reminded him sweetly.

'Ah, yes, though I fear it is disturbing. Last night the Earl attended a soirée at Mrs Yerberry's London mansion. It was an event he would not normally honour with his company, according to my sources, unless he had a special reason. That reason could only be the daughter of the house, Isabelle, a considerable heiress. This morning it was being freely said among milord's servants that he would propose to *her* before the month is out.'

Dominga knew all about Isabelle, thanks to the detailed list of heiresses her father had drawn up for her. 'It's as well I made my move when I did, for if the Earl had solicited her hand first, I'd have had the devil's own job making him recant. An aristocrat thinks nothing of putting a price upon his title when it comes to marriage but his honour, for some extraordinary reason, he considers above purchase.'

'Good god, you don't mean you'd have tried to make him jilt her?' Mr Ponting asked, his voice a shocked whisper. 'I know your father was notorious for his ruthlessness, but not until this moment did I realise how truly you are his daughter.'

Dominga's dimples appeared as she replied: 'Thank you, Mr Ponting. You will never pay me a finer compliment.'

'C-compliment!' he stuttered. 'Think of Miss Yerberry's feelings had the Earl withdrawn an offer for her hand, how shamed and shattered she would have been.'

But Dominga, who had already suffered those emotions because she had once strayed innocently across the path of Hugo Huntsleigh, only replied dryly: 'Any female who goes into a decline because of a man's rough dealing gets only what she deserves, and none of my compassion.'

She saw then that Mr Ponting was looking more shocked than ever, so she went on bracingly: 'Let's waste no more time over something that hasn't happened nor ever will. If my father is to be believed, and I'd doubt the whole world before I doubted him, Miss Yerberry is plump, plain and has a fortune which is insignificant when set beside mine. Moreover, I have the Earl's promise that he will marry me if his lawyers find I am all I appear to be.'

Mr Ponting was about to speak but Dominga silenced him with a wave of her hand. 'Forget Miss Yerberry. She poses no threat to me. The Earl's word is to be trusted. That—' and she smiled as she repeated Hugo's own words—'and nothing else.'

Much as Mr Ponting wanted to believe that his fee was as good as in the bank, caution was so deeply ingrained in his nature that he had to say: 'There is another matter.'

Dominga sighed. 'So there always seems to be with you. Well, let me hear it. It can't be worse than some of the other hazards I have overcome today.'

Mr Ponting coughed discreetly. 'It is a matter of some delicacy.'

'Come to the point,' Dominga said. 'I never knew such a fellow for dancing around something that should be plainly stated.'

'You might find it upsetting,' Mr Ponting warned, for he believed that this wholesome young beauty must be desperately in love with the Earl to pursue him with such tenacity.

However, this further prevarication on his part was met with such a look of irritation from her that he swallowed his scruples and went on: 'The Earl is said to be enamoured of a lovely young French *émigrée*, Désirée, daughter of the late Comte and the Comtesse de Lafayeure.'

'She is not an heiress,' Dominga broke in positively.

'No, but according to my sources she and the Earl fell in love in Brussels before Waterloo. They planned to marry, but after the Earl discovered how deep were the debts he'd inherited the connection became ineligible for both of them. Rumour has it that her need for a rich husband is as great as his need for a rich wife.'

'So the hand that holds the purse-strings holds all,' Dominga mused with satisfaction. 'But this Désirée's name is known to me, although I cannot immediately recall where I have seen it.'

'Her betrothal to a Mr Augustus Marsham has been

announced in the newspapers,' Mr Ponting told her.

Dominga snapped her fingers. 'Of course, that is where I saw it! I took little notice, since I didn't know she had any connection with the Earl. However, if she is to wed another man, why are you so concerned about her?'

'They might yet put aside worldly considerations and run off together. Lovers have been known to do such things,' replied the Job's comforter at her side.

Dominga's eyes flashed with such fire that he almost started trembling again, but the flame was extinguished as soon as she'd had a moment to consider. 'No,' she stated positively, 'that will not happen. The Earl would not have come here had he contemplated such a course of action. She and Miss Yerberry might have indulged a dream or two about marrying him, but it is I who will.'

As they reached the house and she led him towards the dining-room, she added whimsically: 'Pray share my confidence, Mr Ponting, for long faces do not go with good digestions. My step-mama will be disappointed if you permit foolish worries to spoil your luncheon.'

But in this she underestimated her companion. Mr Ponting had all the facility of one who had known poverty to let nothing and nobody come between himself and a square meal. Indeed, no sooner had he been shown his place at the dining-table than he attacked whatever food was within reach as if the shades of those bad old days of his youth were haunting him still.

Nothing could have exceeded his joy when he saw that the luncheon Mrs Romero-Browne had described as 'light' was in fact ample enough to sustain his considerable bulk until he sat at his own table that evening. There were cold meats served with various pickles, a glazed ham, a cold game pie, an omelet and a hot pudding bursting with steak and onions, which was Cecy's particular favourite. In addition there was a jelly, a damson pie, freshly-picked raspberries and cream, a basket of apples and pears, and four different cheeses.

Cecy elected to join the gentlemen in washing down the whole with good home-brewed ale while Dominga sipped daintily at a glass of lemonade. It was not surprising, therefore, that the atmosphere in the dining-room, with its lovingly-polished old furniture and gleaming silver, was rather more mellow than that which had prevailed in the parlour earlier.

Cecy was burning with curiosity to know whether Dominga and Hugo had discussed marriage while they were in the orchard, but she concealed it well since she felt that any reference to the subject should come from the Earl. Once or twice she thought wistfully how lucky the vulgar were, for they dicussed what they wanted when they wanted, with never a thought to what was good or bad taste. As it was, she kept the conversation at the table on such inoffensive subjects as what employment would be found for all the soldiers and sailors now that there was peace, how quickly world trade would revive, and how soon travelling upon the Continent would become fashionable again.

With Dominga ably bearing her part in the discussions, and common civility forcing the Earl to contribute his mite now and again, Mr Ponting was left free to indulge his own particular favourite among the seven deadly sins, namely gluttony. When he was on his second glass of ale and had demolished rather than sampled all of the various dishes, such a feeling of wellbeing spread through him that he began to think there was much to be said, after all, for moving in exalted company.

All he needed to complete his content when they rose from the table was a little nap, but this was denied him. Hugo, impatient to be off, bore him away to the stables. Finding his horses well rested, Hugo had them harnessed to his carriage. He took his leave of his hostess and Dominga in a polite but not prolonged manner, and Cecy could not help noticing that though he bowed slightly over Dominga's hand he did not raise it to his lips. His behaviour, in fact, was as little lover-like as when he had arrived.

Mr Ponting's obsequious farewell lasted for several minutes and might have gone on much longer had he not encountered a look from the Earl, who was already on the curricle with reins in hand, which made him clamber up hurriedly beside him. There was time only for one wave before the horses moved forward at such a smart pace that the ladies were forced to retreat into the house to escape the cloud of dust raised by the curricle's departure.

Cecy, finding herself being propelled towards the parlour by her step-daughter, was wondering apprehensively if milord had depressed all Dominga's pretensions, when a whoop of triumph made her jump.

'Dominga!' she exclaimed. 'You sound as if you are trying to communicate with a savage. Pray have some consideration for my nerves!'

But Dominga was all smiles and no regrets. She closed the parlour door behind them and commanded: 'Congratulate me, Mama. I shall be a countess before the summer is over!'

Cecy sank disbelievingly into the nearest chair. 'Good gracious me! The Earl was very civil to be sure, but I saw no sign of the lover in him.'

'Lover!' Dominga scoffed. 'I am sure they are two a penny, and over-valued at that, but a distinguished husband is harder to secure. However, he desires my money as ardently as I desire his title, so we have settled the matter between us.'

'Wherever did I put my vinaigrette?' Cecy wondered, searching wildly for the pungent salts in her reticule. 'Dear me, what an upsetting day this has been.'

'Surprising,' Dominga corrected. 'What could be upsetting about a day that brings me within reach of my coronet.'

Cecy abandoned her search for the vinaigrette and asked: 'Are you sure you understood him aright?'

'He proposed. What is there to misunderstand about that?'

'But he said not a word to me about it,' Cecy protested indignantly. 'Am I to understand he requested your hand in marriage without first applying to me for permission to do so?'

'I don't think it's in his nature to request anything,' Dominga replied, with her superior knowledge of the Earl, 'and in this case the arrangement is a trifle delicate. It hinges, you see, on his lawyers' satisfactory investigation of my background and financial position. Once that is done, the Earl and I will be married quickly, which suits us both.'

'Your father would not have wished a hole-in-the-corner wedding for you, my dear,' Cecy objected.

'Poof! He would not have cared if I wed in a stable, providing my husband was an aristocrat. Oh, how he would have revelled in the triumph of the Romero-Brownes!'

Cecy couldn't quarrel with that point, but she cautioned: 'If marriage with the Earl is what you truly desire then I am truly happy for you, but if you are just marrying to fulfil your father's wish I fear you will be unhappy.'

'Don't fret on that score. I want the Earl well enough.'

'You love him?' Cecy enquired timidly, not begrudging Dominga a dream come true, although none of her own ever had.

'He is the husband of my own free choice,' Dominga replied ambiguously.

'He is certainly the most handsome man I ever set eyes on,' Cecy had to admit, 'but I cannot be sure he will make you a comfortable husband. Aristocrats do not live as we do and often show a wanton disregard for propriety. I do not wish to nag at you, but I cannot think it wise to marry outside one's class.'

'You did,' Dominga retorted with brutal frankness. 'You are a lady and Papa was never a gentleman.'

Cecy's eyes filled with sadness. 'My case was different. I—I had to take what was offered, you do not.'

Dominga clasped her shoulders and gave her an affectionate little shake. 'What a wretch I am to taunt you so, Cecy, but pray smile for you will soon be well rid of me. As for class, you forget I have been bred to lead an aristocratic life. What is more, I mean to enjoy it to the full. Happiness, like everything else, has to be pursued and I will be no laggard in that race.'

'The Earl's betrothal ring is not yet upon your finger,' Cecy argued. 'Time enough to make plans when it is. To do so now would be premature—and unlucky.'

'What need have I of luck when I have so many other blessings?' Dominga asked arrogantly.

Cecy dived again into her reticule, exclaiming: 'I have a lucky rabbit's foot somewhere!' This time she continued her search until she found it, then held it out to Dominga. 'Do rub it, for I fear so terribly for you when you tempt Providence. You will do it once too often, I know you will!'

But Dominga only laughed and waved the rabbit's foot

away. 'I'd hate my happiness to depend on such a grisly relic. If I pandered to superstition the way you do I'd never get anything achieved. How can you be such a simpleton?'

'How like your father you are. He frightened me at times, too,' Cecy whispered.

Dominga giggled. 'I'm sure he would have told you more forthrightly than I what you may do with your rabbit's foot. Oh, Cecy, do cheer up! To look at your long face you'd think I was about to become a corpse instead of a bride.'

Cecy squealed: 'There you go again! You must not say such things. Truly you must not.'

Dominga threw up her hands. 'What am I to do with you? Will anything defeat this fit of dismals you've inflicted upon yourself?'

Cecy, hopefully rubbing the rabbit's foot against her cheek to placate the wrath of the gods which she was sure Dominga had invoked, gave no answer.

So Dominga, never at a loss for long, came up with one of her own. 'I know, Mama! We will go up to Town and spend so much money you will be too busy worrying over your budget to worry about me. You will buy a dozen new dresses and I, I shall purchase my bride clothes.'

This further example of counting her chickens before they were hatched only produced another wail of protest from Cecy so that Dominga, feeling she had endured enough, left her. She knew that if she took hold of her step-mother again it would not be to shake her affectionately, but to box her ears.

Inevitably, since she liked to live at peace with her little world, Cecy spoke no more of her misgivings and allowed herself to be drawn into her step-daughter's wedding plans with no further protest. And this, of course, meant accompanying her to London.

Normally a visit to the metropolis was a major undertaking for Cecy and involved detailed planning a good month or two before it was scheduled to take place. She considered everything, from the state of the highways due to the weather and the incidence of crime upon them, to choosing a time when her presence at the Manor was not absolutely vital.

Such times were extremely rare, Cecy being one of those

women who could not rid herself of the fear that the very roof would cave in if she absented herself for long. At this time of year there was certainly no lambing or crop-laying to be supervised, but even worse it was high summer, a time when she was usually rooted as firmly at the Manor as one of the trees which sheltered it. There was the harvest coming in, the pickling and the preserving, the laying-up of apples and pears for winter, the stacking of the hay for the animals during the lean months, and other tasks too numerous to mention.

When Cecy, after much serious thought, said at dinner that same evening that she thought she might get away the second week in September if she began planning now, Dominga replied: 'Nonsense. We go tomorrow. I have spoken to John-coachman and the maids are packing now. All you have to do, Mama, is be ready by eight in the morning.'

Cecy's speechless dismay showed that she considered her step-daughter's words as much of a sacrilege as if she had sworn in church. 'I cannot leave here in under six weeks,' she managed at last. 'You have not considered—'

'I have considered everything,' Dominga broke in calmly. 'Let the servants earn their keep. The house won't fall apart nor the farm go to ruin just because you go away for a few days.'

Cecy thought this was rather a sweeping statement and could by no means agree with it, but since she always crumbled before a will stronger than her own she found herself being handed into the carriage promptly at eight the next morning.

Dominga took her place beside her while Harris and Perkins, Cecy's woman, seated themselves opposite with their backs to the horses. John-coachman climbed up on to the box, which he shared with Sam Gibbons who had a lethal-looking blunderbuss beside him.

Even this was not protection enough for Cecy, who believed that the whole world outside Chersey was wicked in the extreme, so two armed outriders on sturdy horses followed the coach as it left the haven of the Manor.

It seemed that everybody in the village turned out to stare at this impressive entourage, and to wave good-bye to the Romero-Browne ladies as enthusiastically as if they were on their way to China instead of London. Indeed, since few of the villagers had not the remotest idea where either place was located, they were sincere in wishing the ladies a safe return from what could only be a den of heathens. Christians, they knew, lived in the village of Popton some five miles along the road, but beyond that who could say?

The sentiments of the villagers were very much in keeping with Cecy's own as the familiar and much-loved scenery was left behind but, even though she was convinced that every highwayman in the country was now converging on the carriage to accost and rob her, she consoled herself with the thought that she had left her best pearls at home.

No such fears troubled Dominga's mind as she leaned back against the luxuriously-padded squabs and reflected how good life was when one had the money to enjoy it. Idly she stroked the red silk upholstery and remembered that this well-sprung travelling chaise had been her father's last gift to her.

He had chosen well, she thought, as he always did, but she must not look back to the past any more. It had been good, but the future had so much more to offer her . . .

CHAPTER
ELEVEN

MUCH to Cecy's surprise and relief the journey proved to be uneventful and, although they stopped for refreshments along the way, the ladies were established before noon in a suite of rooms in an exclusive hotel.

They set forth on their first shopping expedition that very afternoon and began a spending spree which was to last for several days. No dressmaker or milliner patronised by the fashionable was left unvisited, and such were the delights Cecy found in the more exclusive bazaars that she could have spent a whole month going from booth to booth and still found something worthy of her guineas.

Cecy's long years as her brother's housekeeper had taught her, under his eagle eye, how to practise economy to the point of parsimony. By the time she wed Wilfrid, the habit of good-housekeeping was so deeply ingrained that she had lost the knack of being open-handed. But going about town with Dominga she at last learned what joy there could be in purchasing items of delicious nonsense, such as a frivolous bonnet she might never wear or a pair of dainty shoes totally unsuitable for hard country wear. In fact, Cecy quite lost her head and consequently had the time of her life. Among her trophies were gowns, pelisses, bonnets, muffs, gloves, shoes, parasols, reticules, shawls, fans, feathers, brooches. ribands, fringes, spangles, complexion lotions, perfume and scented soaps. When all these, along with Dominga's purchases, were delivered in sundry boxes and packages to their hotel, Dominga laughingly remarked that they would need an extra carriage to take them home.

They spent their evenings quietly, which suited Cecy, although Dominga longed to go to the theatre and opera. She made no complaint, however, for when she brought herself to the attention of Society, she meant it to be as a countess and not a mere country miss.

In response to a missive directed to his City chambers, Mr Ponting visited Dominga one afternoon and told her that the Earl had retired to Hampshire, presumably to ensure that Deversham Hall was ready to receive its new mistress.

His visit was followed by one from her attorney, from whom Dominga learned that no snag had, thus far, been encountered in the dealings with the Earl's lawyers.

With that Dominga had to be content, and when Cecy applied to her bankers for the third time for more funds, she judged it time to retreat to the country.

Cecy chattered her head off all the way home, having seemingly forgotten her misgivings about Dominga actually becoming a countess. It was as if the grey gown she had purchased for the ceremony—after Dominga had told her bluntly that she would not have her fluttering about the church in black like a vulture—had settled the issue in her mind. She had her finery for the wedding, therefore the wedding would take place.

Indeed, as July faded into August and that month rolled on towards September, the ladies' attitudes became reversed, for it was Dominga who began to have disquieting thoughts. She heard nothing from Hugo, nothing at all. Presumably he did not feel the need to further his acquaintance with his intended bride, let alone woo her. By the third week in August she was in such a fever of impatience and uncertainty that she was about to contact her lawyers again, when a morning visit from the Earl's principal attorney made such a course unnecessary.

Mr Alistair Robinson was an incredibly ancient and emaciated man with such a hurried air that Dominga wondered whimsically if he feared the grave would claim him if he sat quietly for a moment. The jerkiness of his movements, coupled with a predilection for springing up unexpectedly, was rather like trying to do business with an uncontrollable jack-in-the-box.

However, the deference with which he greeted her told Dominga all she needed to know. She would be a countess! She felt like throwing herself on his scraggy neck and hugging him, which would certainly have made him jump about more than ever had it not actually brought about his collapse, so it was as well she restrained herself to displaying just the right blend of politeness and reserve suitable for their different stations in life.

Whatever spring juices might once have coursed through Mr Robinson to warm him when he was in the presence of Beauty had clearly dried up long ago, but he was not beyond being impressed by riches. This ensured that, though he was proof against Dominga's loveliness, he would have treated her with respect had she greeted him with the manners and accent of a yokel.

The courtesies dispensed with, and not being prone to flowery eloquence, Mr Robinson promptly got down to the business he had come to conduct on the Earl's behalf.

Not the slightest quiver of relief showed in Dominga's face as he told her that, meticulous investigation having verified all her claims, the wedding could now go ahead. She appeared, if anything, amused as she said: 'My family, not being noble, has always been too respectable to have skeletons rattling around in the cupboards. If that was what you were searching for, sir, I'm sure Deversham Hall would have been a likelier hunting place.'

Mr Robinson did not approve of levity in a young lady, even if she was going to be a countess, so he carried on as if the remark had never been made. Thus it was that Dominga learned that Hugo wished them to be married by special licence at St George's Church, Hanover Square, on Tuesday morning of the following week. There would be no guests, no reception and no honeymoon, since the Earl planned to return immediately to Deversham Hall where he had many urgent estate matters in hand.

Having got this far, Mr Robinson paused. He was expecting a spirited protest—or even tears—from Miss Romero-Browne at her wedding being conducted with such a lack of ceremony. He was surprised when she calmly agreed to the Earl's wishes, although by doing so she was relinquishing all the pomp and ceremony an heiress had a right to expect when she married an earl.

He thought it very odd of her to care so little about what should have been the biggest day of her life, and odder still when she did not turn a hair at hearing there would be no betrothal announcement in the newspapers, no dress party before the wedding, nor even so much as a meeting between the couple until they joined their lives together at the altar, the Earl being far too occupied with other affairs.

However, when he handed over the marriage settlement for her signature, his opinion of her changed from odd to extraordinary. For, although he assured her that the deed had been signed and approved by her own chief attorney, she read every word.

When she paused to re-read a paragraph packed with convoluted legal phrases, he rather patronisingly offered to explain the document to her and was shocked when he was told to be quiet.

Since understanding legal documents was not a necessary accomplishment for a well-bred young lady, and the Earl had scrawled his signature across the deed without giving it so much as a second glance, Mr Robinson was offended. He thought Miss Romero-Browne was a freak, and a dangerous one, for if there were many more like her how was an honest attorney to earn his daily crust? When he saw she had come to the end of the deed, he asked stiffly: 'I trust it has your approval?'

Her brown eyes, when they settled on him, were thoughtful rather than clouded with confusion as she asked: 'Did you draw up this document yourself?'

His bow was his jerkiest yet. The Earl was a valued client, and the goodwill of his countess desirable, but such was Mr Robinson's pride in his work that his hackles rose at the thought of having his skill questioned by a seventeen-year-old chit. 'You have some complaint?' he asked frostily.

'On the contrary, I must compliment you on an excellent piece of work,' she replied sweetly. 'This deed sets out so precisely the arrangement the Earl and I made between us that it can never be contested by either party. Well done, sir. I shall have no scruples in recommending you to any acquaintance of mine who might need an accomplished attorney.'

Mr Robinson, impervious to pretty women as he was, was disarmed, charmed and thoroughly won over. By unerringly finding the only chink in his armour—his pride in his work—she underwent a radical change in his eyes. She was no longer an odd or extraordinary young person, but one of great discernment, scholarship and shrewdness.

The bow with which he accepted her tribute was more courteous than any he had executed for many a long year, and something like fervour crept into his voice as he assured her that it would give him the greatest of pleasure if, some day, he could be of service to *her*.

Dominga smiled and went over to a small writing desk to sign the deed. She intended to win over to her side as many as she could of those people who depended upon the Earl's favour, for one could never tell when one might stand in need of a friend, and she felt she had made a good start with Mr Robinson.

She shook sand over the wet ink of her signature and handed back the document. Mr Robinson replaced it in his travelling bag and produced a small box which, when opened, revealed a ring of great antiquity.

'The Deversham betrothal ring,' he said, not without embarrassment, for it was really the Earl's duty to present it to his chosen one.

Dominga's eyes gleamed when she saw the great ruby encircled by diamonds, not because she lacked splendid jewels of her own, but because it was tangible proof that her dream was about to come true.

There was, however, a hitch. The ring refused to slide over the knuckle of her finger. Hugo's mother, the last to wear this ring, must have been much finer-boned than her successor. Dominga was vexed and tried to force the ring on, but to no avail, so she had to hand it back.

Mr Robinson said placatingly: 'The size of the ring has been altered much from generation to generation. I will have it enlarged before Tuesday's ceremony, and will also ensure that the wedding ring is the right size.'

He rose then, for his business was concluded. Resisting all offers for refreshment, he returned to London with such haste that the Great Reaper himself might have been after him. With him, of course, went the betrothal ring, but Dominga was left with her copy of the marriage settlement to clasp to her bosom. And clasp it she did, most firmly.

'We've done it, Papa,' she whispered aloud, as if the spirit of old Wilfrid was still hovering about the parlour to share in this triumph. 'All your descendants will be noble.' Then, because this high-minded fervour was more than she could sustain, she gave one of those whoops of glee which distressed Cecy so, and added: 'Once, that is, I condescend to let the most noble Earl of Deversham have his way with me.'

The most noble Earl at that moment looked far from sharing Dominga's joy. He was on his way to Town to arrange the last detail concerning the wedding ceremony which was, as far as he was aware, in doubt.

He had moved most of his staff down to Hampshire, where he expected to make a long stay, so there was only the caretaker to bow milord into Deversham House when he arrived. The place was like a tomb, with the furniture under Holland covers and the fine paintings wrapped protectively in brown paper, but Hugo did not go beyond the hall. He paused only long enough to relieve his shoulders of his travelling cape, and the caretaker's mind by saying he would be lunching and dining out, before setting off again, this time on foot.

Hugo's destination was the lodgings in Duke Street of Major Sir Giles Millichip, a baronet under whom he had served in the Hussars, and his best friend. He struck lucky, for the Major was not only off duty but at home. His man, knowing Hugo well, took him straight upstairs after saying the Major was just about to stroll round to his club.

It quite wrung Hugo's heart to be back in the bachelor atmosphere of a serving officer's civilian lodgings, for he had recently given up just such a set of rooms himself.

The Major's back was to the door as Hugo was admitted to the sitting-room and he did not turn immediately for he was studying his splendid moustachios in the mirror over the mantel before declaring himself fit to be seen abroad.

He was a tall man, taller even than Hugo, but he was so extremely thin that his shoulders had developed a stoop as if the burden of them was too much for him to bear. The mustard coat he wore had been cleverly cut and subtly padded to disguise this defect, for he was a man of fashion and could afford to indulge his whims.

His legs might lack the shape to do full justice to his pale yellow pantaloons, but no fault could be found with his tasselled Hessian boots, nor with the intricate folds of his cravat between his starched collar points.

It amused the Major to cultivate an air of languor and to appear as little more than an empty-headed dandy, but those who had served with him knew that the hand which now held a snuffbox so gracefully was equally at home doing savage work with a sabre. He was, in fact, as much of a goer in battle as he was in fashion, so that while his fellow officers eyed him with amused indulgence, he had the respect of all of them.

'By Jove, Chips, you look like a curst canary!' Hugo exclaimed irreverently.

The Major turned, put down the snuffbox and crossed the room with rapid strides to wring Hugo's hand with an energy surprising in one so languid. 'Damned lot you know about it,' he retorted. 'You look like something the dog should have left outside the door. But where have you been hiding yourself, dear boy? Half the town is saying that you've blown your brains out, while the other half maintains there's no need since a certain heiress is to have the honour of towing you out of the River Fleet.'

The smile faded from Hugo's face as he replied ruefully: 'I wish I knew which fate was worse, the bullet or the Yerberry brat. Which would you herald as your salvation, Chips?'

Major Millichip looked at once conscience-stricken. 'Forgive me, Hugo. I know I don't have to stand on ceremony with you, but that was a deuced silly thing to say. No doubt you came to me for a breathing space, eh, a time in which to forget it all? Good fellow, I'm due for a lark myself. Shall we set forth this instant to make London as lively as Brussels was before the battle?'

'I'm game, but there's something I must talk to you about first, if you have the manners to offer me a chair,' Hugo replied.

The Major raised the quizzing glass which hung from a long riband around his neck and surveyed Hugo from his dust-covered boots and breeches to the creases in his blue coat and his carelessly tied cravat.

'You come to me in all your travel dirt and dare to revile my manners?' he marvelled. 'Stanton would have a fit if he could see you now. I'm not sure I'm far from a spasm myself. However, have a seat if that's your pleasure. My man can always consign it to the street afterwards.'

Hugo greeted this stricture with a grin and flung himself into an armchair. Chips seated himself opposite with a great deal more care since he had too much respect for his coat to encourage the cloth to wrinkle, a manoeuvre which only made Hugo remark with a shocking disrespect for his former senior officer: 'What a fop you are, Chips. I'm surprised you can bear to put your uniform aside.'

'It is a wrench,' Chips admitted. 'I agree that no sight can equal that of a Hussar officer, but upon occasion one can achieve creditable results with civilian togs. You must try it yourself sometime.'

Hugo laughed. 'I doubt if even London could withstand the shock of two canaries strutting about. But to get down to business, Chips—'

The Major restrained him with one hand upheld and called for his man to bring decanters and glasses. When the tray was on a table by his side, and the servant had retreated, he said: 'Malaga to start with, Hugo?' Receiving a nod, he selected two glasses, poured, and when both of them were leaning back with a glass in hand, invited: 'Well, my impetuous young friend, what is on your mind?'

Now that he had the opening he wanted, Hugo prevaricated. 'How's your wound?' he asked.

Chips glanced down at his left hand, which was clad in a specially made glove since he'd had part of the outer palm and two fingers sliced neatly from it at Waterloo. 'I can't wear as many rings as I used to,' he complained, 'but one adjusts. And your wound?'

'It was never worth the stitches that that cow-handed butcher set in it, but it healed cleanly, which makes me a lot luckier than some,' Hugo replied, sipping his sherry. 'Truth is, I've forgotten all about it, which is just as well for I haven't come to talk about that.'

'Didn't for a moment think you had,' the Major confessed, his eyes gleaming with an intelligence not often revealed to the world. 'I've heard how things stand with you and—' he coughed discreetly—'I beg you to remember that I'm pretty well-heeled if I can be of service to you in that way.'

Hugo launched himself from his chair with an explosive oath and began to pace about the room. 'God! Do you think I've come to play the beggar to my friends? You know me better than that, Chips!'

'Yes,' the Major replied quietly, 'but since I am a friend I thought I could make such an offer without giving offence. I beg your pardon.'

Hugo ran a hand through his already rumpled hair. 'Let me beg yours. I'm not myself, I fear, or maybe I'm too much myself! I always was dashed touchy on my pride.'

Chips smiled. 'And dashed restless, too. Sit down, there's a good fellow, and have some more sherry. It might pacify you and thus soothe my nerves.'

'Nerves? You?' Hugo snorted derisively. 'Try fooling somebody else. I know you too well to confuse an affectation with an affliction.'

'You leave me nothing to say,' Chips drawled, 'unless to invite you once more to unburden your mind of its cares.'

'I came to ask you to be my groomsman,' Hugo said abruptly.

There was an infinitesimal pause before his friend answered: 'Gladly. I'd be honoured.' He looked down into the rich amber of his sherry as he added: 'Is it to be Miss Yerberry?'

Hugo drained his glass. 'It very nearly was but, 'struth, Chips, the bullet would have been the better choice! You've met the mama. Enough said, eh? Between the pair of them they'd have driven me to drink or the Colonies within six months.'

The Major smiled slightly. 'You always did have your way of putting things, but I can't deny I'm relieved you've escaped that fate. Who *is* to be your bride, then? Do I know her?'

Hugo sprang from his chair again and began to stride around the furniture in the manner his friend deplored. 'No, you don't know her. She's a Cit's daughter, but her mother was a Spanish gentlewoman so there's good blood on that side. The mother died donkey's years ago and the step-mother's a lady, a Reverson out of Kent. You know the family?'

Chips nodded, concealing his astonishment well, for

none knew better than he what agonies his haughty young friend must have gone through before deciding to ally himself with a product of the merchant class.

Hugo went on quickly: 'The girl's name is Dominga Romero-Browne, which makes her sound half flash and half foolish, but she's neither. She has looks and style and, well, her father died recently and left her a fortune several times larger than Isabelle Yerberry's.'

Again the Major said nothing and Hugo, his face set into a mask to conceal his emotions, added: 'The money is the sugar that coats the pill. You know how I feel about Désirée, and why I had to give her up, and Miss Romero-Browne was the best choice I could make in the circumstances.'

Hugo slumped down into the armchair and watched moodily as the Major removed the sherry glasses, replaced them with brandy glasses, and poured out the more potent liquor from another decanter. All this was done in Chips's usual lazy way, but his brain was busy. He had known Hugo too long to be unaware of the anguish he was suffering, and yet he applauded the resolution with which he was acting.

Once or twice Chips had roused himself sufficiently to fall in love and he knew what torture that tender emotion could inflict, but he was enough of a realist to believe that while women came and went, duty was the rock a wise man clung to. A noble line like Deversham's should be upheld because it would still be there long after any feminine charms which threatened it had crumbled into dust. Even so, Chips wished there was some way he could alleviate Hugo's misery and finally uttered the only words of solace he could think of: 'The Yerberry mama is going to be as mad as fire.'

He was rewarded by the boyish grin which spread over Hugo's face. 'Won't she just!' he exclaimed. 'Serves her right for trying to order me about like a schoolboy when I went to one of her damnably dull *soirées*.'

'I'd like to see her face when she hears an unknown heiress has stolen the coronet from under Isabelle's nose,' the Major went on, replenishing the glasses as if the discomfiture of Mrs Yerberry was something worth drinking to. 'She's been puffing off her hopes all over Town, as if the marriage was a certainty.'

'It does me good to be with you,' Hugo asserted warmly, swirling the brandy around in his glass and then drinking it. 'I won't pretend I'm overjoyed with this match because I'm not, but there's some sort of compensation in being able to tweak that old harpie's nose. Makes me feel I've made the best I could of a bad job.'

The Major could find no fault with this sentiment, although he felt that Hugo was not going into his marriage in quite the happy frame of mind he would have wished for him. He raised the brandy decanter and studied the level of the liquid remaining within.

'Tell you what, Hugo,' he drawled, 'better let me have the particulars of the ceremony while we're both still sober enough to remember 'em.'

'Ten o'clock next Tuesday at St George's, Hanover Square. No fuss, no guests, no banns. Special licence affair to get it over with as quietly and quickly as possible. There's to be no announcement in the papers, either, until afterwards. I don't care to be gawked at by the idle and the curious.'

The Major, dredging up from a slightly clouded mind what he knew of rich young women and the stir they liked to cause in Society, asked: 'Miss Romero-Browne does not object?'

'Why should she object?' Hugo expostulated. 'She's going to be a countess, dammit. That's enough for any woman.'

If the Major thought that, for all his experience, Hugo had a dashed funny notion about women, he held his peace. After all, Hugo knew his bride and if she responded to his high-handed methods, then presumably she approved of them.

When the two gentlemen set out some half-hour later for one of their clubs, it was as if they had nothing heavier on their minds than bespeaking a luncheon before pursuing some kind of entertainment with which to while away the rest of the day. Neither of them referred to the forthcoming marriage, having both privately decided that Tuesday morning at St George's would be time enough to think of it again.

CHAPTER
TWELVE

DOMINGA was even more radiant than a bride was expected to be, and the vibrant tone with which she made her vows echoed around the empty church. Beside her, Hugo was as pale as death. It was necessary to strain the ear to hear what he said, for the time-honoured words seemed so distasteful to him that they had to be forced through unwilling lips. But the clergyman officiating at the ceremony heard him, and so did the sweetly-smiling Dominga, and that was all that mattered.

Cecy wept, of course, but not from grief at losing her step-daughter. It was the lack of full wedding regalia that her soft heart sorrowed for, and the soullessness of the vacant pews.

At the back of the church, clad as resplendently as a dowager in purple satin and with more feathers in her bonnet than she had ever dared to wear before, Harris felt nothing but satisfaction as she witnessed the nuptials which would give her a prime position at the table in the servants' hall at Deversham Hall. Stanton, next to her, felt more mixed emotions. He knew the bride was not the one his master had wished to share his life with, but now that Stanton had seen her for himself he could not understand why the Earl should put such a gallow's face upon the whole proceedings. Miss Romero-Browne was as wholesome and toothsome a package as Stanton had seen in many a long day and half-English and half-Spanish was, to his patriotic mind, better than all-French could ever be.

As for Major Millichip, it was something of a miracle that he remembered to produce the ring at the right moment for he had sustained a considerable shock. Ringing through his ears were not the words being spoken at the altar, but those of Hugo's on their day of Bacchanalia when he'd confided that he regarded his wedding as making the best of a bad job.

Such a sentiment expressed by the bridegroom was hardly likely to prepare the Major for the Vision that had walked down the aisle on the arm of the Reverend Jonathan Reverson, Cecy's brother, on whom had fallen the honour of giving the bride away.

To Chips's dazzled eyes the bridge was beauty personified, walking poetry, a goddess descended from Olympian heights—and Hugo was the luckiest dog alive.

Any man other than a star-crossed lover would have thought so, too, for Dominga glowed in a morning gown of magnolia silk and the brim of her matching bonnet framed her lovely face like a halo. In one hand she carried a small bunch of hothouse rosebuds, the only splash of colour about her save for the vividness of her own natural colouring.

The Major, gallant enough to figuratively fall on his knees and worship before any shrine of feminine excellence, could only marvel that Hugo appeared so impervious to his bride's charms. Here, surely, was the very maiden who could break Désirée's hold upon his heart and bring him happiness as well as riches.

And so, when Chips produced the wedding ring, it was with more hope and heartiness than he'd expected to feel as he performed his small but vital task.

But Hugo's face was an expressionless mask and the set of his shoulders rigid as he slid the binding band of gold on Dominga's finger. His eyes had a faraway look as if they were trying to glimpse for one last time the paradise that might have been, had Désirée been the bride beside him now. Never had a man been more wretched than Hugo when, having given his heart to one woman, he gave his name to another.

If Hugo felt he was at rock bottom, Dominga was experiencing an emotional peak. Exultantly she relived the scene in the inn at Chersey when she and Hugo had been joined in a passion which had led through her own conniving to this legal union today.

She shook a little with excitement as she remembered those mad moments, then shock ran through her anew as she saw again his guineas showering down upon her. Well, she had another piece of gold from him now and it was safely round her finger, where it would remain as long as she lived as proof that there were some women a rake would be wiser not to trifle with.

A brief blessing was given and the ceremony was over, but neither bride nor groom moved, so caught up were they in scenes from another time and place. It took a discreet cough from Chips to recall them to their present surroundings, and Cecy mopped her eyes while the register was duly signed and witnessed.

No triumphal burst of organ music accompanied Dominga and Hugo back down the aisle, but neither of them missed it. The groom would have regarded it as a mockery, while the bride had triumph tapping out its own happy beat in her heart.

Outside the church, hands were shaken and congratulations offered and received. Dominga found her hand clasped by the Major who was telling her that his friends, and he hoped he might now count her among them, called him Chips. She smiled and thanked him with such a pleasing huskiness of voice and such a warm smile that he was further convinced that Hugo would not for long lament his lost love.

Cecy claimed his attention then, and Dominga was free to let her eyes dwell gloatingly upon her husband. He might have been a reluctant bridegroom, but he was an extremely elegant one. He had taken unusual pains with his appearance, much in the manner of one of his ancestors who had looked his best for his last appearance upon the scaffold in medieval times.

Dominga knew nothing of that ancestor, but she did approve of Hugo's superbly-cut blue coat, his pale pantaloons, his gleaming Hessians, and the neat arrangement of his cravat. Chips, who was similarly attired, had wanted the bridegroom to embellish his appearance with a diamond pin, fob and snuff box, but Hugo had told him curtly that he had no intention of being turned into a curst court card.

Even so, he was handsome enough and his bride beautiful enough to attract the attention of passers-by, and so soon as Hugo saw a crowd was beginning to gather he hurried rather than handed Dominga into his travelling chaise. The door with the Deversham coat of arms emblazoned upon the panel was closed, the last farewells were said, and the young couple began their journey to Hampshire.

The group they left behind did not linger long, either. Cecy entered her own carriage to return to Chersey Manor which she could, at last, wholly regard as her own. Not being a socially ambitious woman her thoughts did not dwell on the triumph of her step-daughter becoming a countess, though her brother could talk of little else, but on how pleasant and comfortable her life would be now that she no longer had to worry what scrape Dominga would get into next.

Harris and Stanton got into Dominga's travelling carriage, which was to follow the Earl's equipage to Deversham Hall, while Major Millichip set off on a round of his clubs. There he spread the news that his good friend Deversham had just carried off the most ravishing and rich bride of the century, let alone the year, god damn and bless his luck.

The news spread like fire through Society and when Mrs Yerberry heard it her wrath spilled over her hapless daughter's head. Isabelle dutifully cried, but her tears were of profound relief and, if she trembled, it was for Hugo's bride rather than for herself.

Isabelle could not thank her guardian angel enough for ensuring that she would be sleeping safely in her own bed this night while some unknown heiress would be at the mercy of the Earl, who discomposed her so with his suppressed vitality and glittering blue eyes.

While her mother raged that Hugo had made a laughing stock of her—though, in fact, it was her own loose tongue that was largely responsible—Isabelle began to hope that they would retire to the country until her mother felt strong enough to face her friends again.

When Désirée heard that Hugo had married a young lady as beautiful as she was rich, she flew into a passion that matched Mrs Yerberry's for heat. Désirée might be only two weeks from her own wedding, but to have a rival for Hugo's love provoked her into storming about her room and throwing things at her maid, until that unfortunate

person gave up trying to placate her and fled in fear of her
life.

Only then did Désirée calm down enough to evaluate the
intelligence that had been brought to her. The facts as they
had been related to her were that only Major Millichip and
two of the bride's relations had witnessed the ceremony,
and that it was from the Major that such a flattering
description of the bride had been gleaned.

Désirée was aware that Chips was Hugo's best friend,
and that either would support the other whatever befell
them. Was it not possible, then, that Chips's description of
the bride might have been kinder than if some other man
had married her? Désirée rather thought so.

Allowing also for exaggeration as the story spread, it
really was not surprising that the bride had been flattered
beyond belief by the time her description reached such an
outpost as Wimbledon. Désirée sought her mirror for
reassurance and, after studying herself from every angle
and finding all of them perfect, her equilibrium was restored. No woman, she was sure, could match her for looks
and so oust her from Hugo's heart.

She knew her man, and judged him too fastidious to feel
affection for any low-born heiress—and the bride must be
such or Hugo would never have married her in such a
furtive fashion. No doubt he had chosen her rather than
Miss Yerberry so that he could bury her in rural Hampshire, for he would never appear among the *ton* with a
vulgar woman on his arm, even if she was his wife.

With these soothing thoughts, Désirée began to count
the days to her own wedding for then, with the necessary
legal unions behind them, she and Hugo would be able to
resume their *affaire* where circumstances had forced them
to leave off.

Désirée would have felt even more complacent had she
known that a long expanse of blue upholstery separated
Hugo from his bride as they travelled down to Deversham
Hall. Dominga sat in one corner and he lolled in the other
and neither descended from the coach when the horses
were changed for the first time. Neither did they speak,
though when they were on their way again Dominga
glanced covertly at her husband.

He was as pale as he had been during the ceremony, and though any bride could be expected to be daunted by setting out on a new life with such a grim-faced bridegroom, Dominga's thoughts were as rosy as her cheeks. She had willingly cut off every connection with her old life save for Harris, and the only wrench she had felt was when she'd bid adieu to Sam Gibbons. It was not Dominga's way to develop a close relationship with those who served her, but for Gibbons she felt a genuine affection.

However, her marriage meant that he had come into the inheritance that would set him up in the business he desired and he would no longer have to touch his forelock to anybody if it did not suit him to do so. Gibbons was not one of those who, having found a comfortable niche, will happily stagnate in it and ask no more of the world. He wished to progress, as Dominga did, and she respected him for it and cast no rub in his way. Still, she uttered a sigh for the one person she felt was truly a friend.

Hugo heard that sigh and made a gallant attempt to wrench himself from his wretched thoughts. He could not spend his life looking backwards. He had made his bed and even if he had to lie in it alone for a year, it would be foolish to make it more uncomfortable than necessary.

He had to live with this Dominga Romero-Browne—no, Dominga Huntsleigh now!—and he could not go on churlishly ignoring her. No further sigh came from her, but Hugo knew that if she could be kept content and at the same time reasonably out of his way, the tenor of his life would not be too drastically altered.

'I have been thinking, madam,' he began, then broke off as he realised he could scarcely tell her exactly what he had been thinking. That was no way to negotiate a pact with her.

Dominga was amused. So . . . he could still not bring himself to use her name, but it would be politic to accept 'madam' as an improvement on 'miss'. She said: 'You have been thinking, perhaps, that a marriage of convenience should be lived out in a manner as convenient as possible to both parties?'

Hugo was astounded at her astuteness and, being Hugo, he snapped: 'You're a damned knowing one.'

'For thinking along the same lines as you?' she asked. 'I don't see what's remarkable about that. It was just a case of which of us made the first push to say what must be said.'

She paused to let these words sink in, then added deliberately: 'I am a countess now, which is what I wanted, but it won't amuse me if everybody can perceive as readily as I can that my husband is sulking.'

'I am not sulking,' Hugo denied, stung.

'You are,' Dominga continued calmly. 'What is more, I don't think it would amuse you, either, to appear before your friends in such a light. In fact, only the world would be amused.'

She was so right that Hugo was silenced. Having married to shoulder the responsibilities of his estates, he must now take up also all the responsibilities of having a wife.

When he spoke again he sounded older, wearier and wiser than he ever had before: 'I shall not give anybody cause to whisper against you. You are my wife now, and your position and authority will be upheld in a proper manner. It is my duty to do so and—' he ended on a less high-minded and more bitter note—'today's business has proved I know how to do my duty.'

Dominga was satisfied. Hugo's support, whatever he might privately feel, was essential if she was to establish herself effectively in her new role. 'We are agreed, then, that publicly we will appear content while privately we'll be civilised enough to deal as amiably as possible together?'

Hugo nodded. Appearances must be kept up. Much as he would have loved to scandalise the world by running off with Désirée, when the moment of decision had come he had chosen to conform—and must continue to do so. And so he finally swallowed the bitter pill of his marriage, but, for all its sugar-coating, it left him with a sour taste. He groaned: 'I am not the man I thought I was.'

Dominga frowned. 'What can you mean?'

He glanced at her with such pain in his eyes that she was startled. 'That it was much easier to be a younger son than to be the Earl of Deversham.'

She could not believe he was in earnest, and exclaimed: 'You cannot be sorry that you succeeded to the title?'

'I was never more sorry for anything in my life.'

He spoke with such uncharacteristic wistfulness that Dominga was sure he was not yearning for his army days, but for the woman who went with them. The French girl Horace Ponting had spoken of, Mademoiselle Désirée de Lafayeure.

No compassion stirred within her. Perhaps this was because, locked deep inside her, was the pain Hugo had inflicted on her two years before when he had taken only her body and rejected the love she had been so ready to give. But, whether it was pain or pride which drove her on, she would crush his love for Désirée as thoroughly as she would crush anything that stood in the way of her full revenge. Yet she must be subtle about it. Having been goaded into rejecting him as a proper husband for a year, she could hardly throw herself at his head. It would be too contradictory.

Dominga settled back into her corner to consider ways in which she could slowly drive him mad with desire for her and, by the time the coach stopped for a second change of horses, she had thought of many.

This time Hugo handed her out of the coach and led her into the inn, where he hired a private parlour and ordered refreshments. They seated themselves at the table more like polite strangers than bride and groom and spoke little as they ate the best cold meal the establishment could offer at such short notice.

Still, the break in the journey was not without effect, for the way in which the menials bowed and scraped about them, and the innkeeper's insistence upon serving them himself, gave Dominga her first taste of what it was like to be a countess.

The second taste came when they arrived at Deversham Hall. The original medieval hall which had given the house its name had been added to considerably in Tudor times, then embellished further during the Stuart dynasty. Now, however, all this was tucked behind an entirely new wing which had all the exquisite proportions of Georgian architecture, and which had been erected by Hugo's grandfather.

It was before the great front doors of this wing that the chaise stopped while liveried servants ran out to let down

the steps so that the master of all this grandeur could help
his bride to alight into the afternoon sunshine.

Dominga paused to look about her. The house, with
terraces below the driveway leading down to a beautiful
ornamental lake, was set in a park which encompassed the
whole of a shallow valley. With such a home to preside
over, and with such a husband to lead her through the front
door, Dominga decided that she had had full value for her
money.

Indeed, she felt more like a queen than a countess as she
moved forward to shake hands with the principal servants
who were lined up in the entrance hall to greet her with
proper respect. She had a few words for the steward, the
butler, the housekeeper and the cook before she progres-
sed along the line, noting carefully the names and faces and
displaying remarkable self-possession.

She showed no blushing confusion, nor any sign at all
that she found this ritual something of an ordeal, which the
senior servants might have been forgiven for expecting
from so young a bride. But then, they had already been
taken off guard by her beauty. It was no secret to them that
their master had married because of financial necessity, and
like Major Millichip they could only marvel that the bride
scarcely needed money to recommend her.

Dominga allowed them all a good look, lingered long
enough to say all the right things, then allowed the housekeeper to take her up the great curved staircase to her suite
of rooms. She found herself in a large and elegant sitting-
room which had gilded and painted panels on the walls and
ceiling, and long windows which were opened on to a
balcony to let in whatever breeze stirred on this hot, late
August day.

Her bedroom was equally large so that it was scarcely
dwarfed by the silk-draped, befrilled and beribboned four-
poster bed which would have dominated a room of less lofty
and spacious proportions. After this there was only the
dressing-room to inspect which, Mrs Chandler told her
discreetly, adjoined the Earl's dressing-room.

Dominga eyed the housekeeper consideringly as she
wondered whether she would be an enemy or an ally. Mrs
Chandler had a great deal of dignity, as befitted her posi-

tion in the household, but she had pleasant features and looked approachable.

'How long have you been at Deversham Hall?' Dominga asked as a way of establishing some personal contact between them.

'Since the Restoration, my lady,' Mrs Chandler replied. Seeing Dominga's startled expression, her own relaxed into a smile. 'I was forgetting that you wouldn't know I was born a Leggett. I'm the steward's sister, and our family has served the Earl's since Charles the Second's time.'

'I see . . .' Dominga replied, perceiving that she would have to tread very warily indeed. 'And your husband?'

'Dead these five years, my lady, but I've two grown-up daughters to lighten my sorrow. The eldest is my assistant here and the youngest is housekeeper to Sir Rollo Sutherton, who lives at The Grange, not six miles away.'

Dominga murmured something appropriate as she walked back into her private sitting-room. The suite was decorated throughout in pink and, although she liked the delicate French furniture, it bore the stamp of a personality totally different to her own. She knew that Hugo's mother had died some ten years before and, apparently, nothing had been changed since her passing.

Dominga looked again at Mrs Chandler and decided to be frank. 'Pink is not my colour so it will have to be changed. We'll have the decorators in as soon as possible, if you please. Another bedchamber can be prepared for me while the work is being carried out.'

Mrs Chandler was taken aback. She had expected changes, of course, and had schooled herself to accept them without fuss, but she had not expected a bride who hadn't yet been bedded to assert herself so soon. Like many long-established servants, she was set in her ways and therefore instinctively opposed to having anything altered, so it cost her a lot to drop a curtsy and merely reply: 'Yes, my lady.'

Dominga, satisfied that she had established who was mistress here now, promptly turned on the charm. 'We shall have a merry time, the two of us, consulting pattern cards and deciding on fabrics and colours. You must guide me if I am in doubt, for I'm sure you have far more experience in such matters than I have.'

Mrs Chandler thawed instantly and was assuring her new
mistress that she'd be pleased to help in any way she could
when a knock at the door heralded Harris's arrival, followed by footmen bearing Dominga's luggage.

Within a few minutes, the housekeeper had been dismissed, the footmen had gone away and Harris was establishing herself and her mistress in their new domain.

Dominga sat down at the dressing-table with a little sigh
of satisfaction. 'I'll wear the white gown with red ribbons
for dinner. See that it is unpacked first.'

Country hours were kept at Deversham Hall, which
meant that dinner was served at six o'clock, much earlier
than the fashionable would have tolerated in Town. When
Dominga left her rooms at half-past five, a footman was
hovering in the wide passage to conduct her to the Crimson
Saloon, where it was customary for the family to gather
before dinner.

As Dominga went down the grand staircase she looked
every inch a countess. She had never allowed her hair to be
cut and tortured into bunches of ringlets, as was the
fashion, and tonight it was swept up into braids held by a
ruby ornament, which went well with the enlarged betrothal ring now keeping her wedding band company on her
finger.

Her skin was as soft and glowing as her white silk gown
which, had it not been for the red ribbon slotted through
lace on the low neck and high waistline, might have been
the bridal dress she had been denied of wearing that
morning.

Her back was straight and her head was high as she was
bowed into the Crimson Saloon by the footman. Then the
door was closed behind her and she was alone with her
husband.

Hugo, even with memories of Désirée teasing his heart,
would have been less than human if he had not been struck
by his bride's magnificence. Besides her obvious charms
she had style, superb dress sense, and something else as
well—an intangible quality which he possessed himself, a
kind of magnetism which drew immediate attention.

It was impossible to be unaware of her, just as she found

it impossible to be unaware of him. Consequently they eyed each other warily, just as two well-matched opponents might eye each other when they stepped into the prize-ring.

Hugo lifted a decanter. 'Sherry?' he asked with nothing more than the civil politeness he might have used for a total stranger.

Dominga nodded. She came further into the room and sat down gracefully on a sofa, its crimson upholstery making a perfect setting for her. She took the glass he offered and sipped it cautiously. She did not care for alcohol, preferring to keep a clear head at all times. Muddled thinking, her father had taught her, was not for schemers who wished to be successful.

Hugo, apparently, was in no hurry to make conversation, but eventually he asked: 'I trust you find your rooms comfortable?'

Dominga began to feel vaguely irritated. She preferred him angry, sulky—anything but so studiously polite that he was just a shade away from insolence.

'Comfortable, but not satisfactory. They will have to be redecorated,' Dominga replied.

Hugo's eyebrows snapped together. Whatever he had expected from his bride, it was not criticism of his home. 'My mother was happy enough in them,' he said.

'I'm sure she was, but anybody who could live among all those pink frills must have been a very different woman to me.'

'Indubitably. She was a lady,' Hugo replied.

'Did she also have the honour of rescuing her husband from debt?' Dominga enquired with deadly sweetness.

'How like a Cit to bring the conversation round to money at every conceivable opportunity,' he observed. 'It's what disgusts the *ton* so particularly. If you wish to reach the inner circle of Society you'll have to learn not to reveal you are a merchant's daughter every time you open your mouth. Since you are my wife you'll be forgiven all manner of eccentricities, but never vulgarity.'

Dominga bit her lip in fury. He saw, and smiled in such a way that the truce they had made in the chaise was shattered beyond repair. It seemed there was no way they could live at peace with each other, even under so large a roof as Deversham Hall provided.

'My trick?' Hugo suggested with maddening amusement.

Dominga was saved from having to concede she'd lost the clash of words by Jamieson, the butler, entering to announce that dinner was served. The double doors which led into the dining-room were opened, each flanked by a footman.

Hugo did not take his bride's hand to lead her through and, indeed, she had to rise rather hurriedly to ensure that she was at least in her rightful place by his side as they passed through the doors.

There was a grand dining-room and a smaller one, which was used when the family dined alone, and this was the one they entered now. Even so, a dozen people could have sat in relatively isolated splendour at the table. When Hugo sat in the great carved chair at the head of the table and Dominga in one only slightly less splendid at the foot, conversation between them was as impractical as either of them could have wished. Moreover, a massive epergne decorated artistically with flowers and fruit was so sited in the centre of the table that they could not see each other, either.

Had Désirée been his bride, Hugo would probably have consigned the epergne to a cellar and ordered her place to be set next to his but, as it was, he made no complaint. Dominga was left to glower at the flowers and fruit, and only the butler and the footmen were able to admire the daintiness with which she ate her food.

Mrs Barrows, the cook, not knowing the tastes of the new Countess, had done her best to offer something which would be found acceptable. There was potted shrimps, poached eggs with a ham sauce, baked fish, braised duck with green peas, roast beef with florets of cauliflower, tongue with cherry sauce, cold partridges, apple fritters, a meringue, ice cream, pastries, several supporting side-dishes and a variety of sauces.

Jamieson, with a sense of occasion, kept the Earl's glass flowing with champagne, but he could see the Countess was no lover of the sparkling wine for she scarcely touched her glass.

Her appetite, however, was seemingly unimpaired by bridal nerves, for although she refused some dishes she ate a goodly portion of those she accepted. When she rose from the table she was conducted to the Blue Saloon, which offered every comfort from deep armchairs to card tables so that the hours after dinner and before bedtime could be whiled away as pleasantly as possible.

The Earl remained at the dining-table, ignoring the port and brandy that were set before him after the covers had been removed, and continued to drink his way steadily through the bottle of champagne.

As time passed, the servants could not fail to notice that he appeared in no hurry to join his bride. Neither, for that matter, could Dominga.

She did not care for tatting or knitting or, indeed, for any of those pastimes with which ladies were accustomed to occupy themselves. She did have a tapestry in a frame, but it was as yet unpacked. Besides, when she set stitches in it, it was more as a matter of form than pleasure. It would not have pleased her, either, to sit tamely stitching on her wedding night until such time as it pleased her lord to join her.

By the time the light had faded and a servant came in to attend to the candles, Dominga had had enough. She asked to be taken to the library, had the candles lighted there also and dismissed the servant.

One glance at the ancient furniture and the heavy tomes lining the walls told her that this was a masculine domain. No doubt Hugo would resent her presence here. The impulse to remain, rather than to return to the Blue Saloon with a book as she had intended, naturally became irresistible. She found a copy of Byron's *Hours of Idleness*, thought it appropriate, and settled down to read it.

When Hugo eventually found her there he looked angrily about the room as if it had in some way been defiled, and there was more than champagne behind the glitter in his eyes as he said: 'It is the custom of the ladies of this house to await the gentlemen in the Blue Saloon after dinner.'

'How very obliging of them,' Dominga returned affably, 'but as I am the only lady of this house at the moment, and it is not *my* custom to await anybody anywhere when I am bored, you must either entertain me or expect me to find some entertainment for myself.'

Hugo's jaw jutted. 'I will not have you setting this house by the ears. You will conform or . . .' He broke off deliberately, to let the unspoken threat hover in the air between them, but Dominga was amused rather than intimidated.

'Or what?' she challenged. 'Do you have dungeons you would cast me into? How very gothic, but I don't think even an Earl of Deversham could get away with a bride disappearing on her wedding night.'

Hugo did not care to be mocked and he said dangerously: 'There are many other ways in which I can teach you to obey me.'

'Then I must pray that they are more diverting than the Blue Saloon,' Dominga replied, rising to her feet. 'However, now that I have found a book to occupy myself with I've no objection to returning there. I think you've already given the servants sufficient food for gossip by remaining alone at the table for so long.'

He glowered at her, but she smiled blandly at him and allowed herself to be conducted back to the Blue Saloon in grim silence, a silence which lasted long after she had settled herself down once more with her book.

Hugo did not offer to play cards, nor anything, but instead fidgeted about the room until he came to rest against a window, moodily pulling back the curtains so that he could gaze out over the moonlit garden. The sun had at last set on this dreadful day, but there was still some time to go until he could be decently done with it.

He wondered if he would feel more married on the morrow, more resigned, but doubted it since it would be a year until he had a proper wife. These thoughts made him turn his head to study his bride again.

She had proved already that she could ably defend herself with words and had shown flashes, upon occasion, of having a temperament as fiery as his own. She would not be an easily managed partner and he wondered if he had not made a mistake, after all, in choosing her rather than Isabelle.

And yet he knew that had it been Isabelle here with him,

he could not have borne to look at her at all. As it was, it was all he could do to drag his eyes away from Dominga's desirable form. He might not love her, but she did arouse in him the natural passion any healthy young man could expect to feel when in the presence of a well-proportioned female. He could readily imagine what it would feel like to touch her smooth white neck, her bare arms.

Dominga, her eyes fastened on her book but nonetheless aware of his burning gaze, moved slightly so that her neckline slipped a little, exposing with apparent innocence one perfect shoulder.

Hugo's eyes fastened on it avidly and desire rose urgently within him for this bride he had sworn not to touch. He waited for the return of the loathing which had made the promise so easy to make at the time, but it didn't come.

He tried to tear his eyes from her and couldn't, so that what loathing he did feel was for himself. How could he, who loved Désirée, feel lust for the woman he had unwillingly married?

But for once all images of Désirée, which might have saved him, refused to be conjured up. His dark-haired, dark-eyed bride filled his eyes and his mind until the very silence between them seemed to be pulsing through his ears to the beat of his own desires. What he might have done had not the arrival of the tea-tray recalled him to himself he did not dare to guess, but he turned back to the window as a fine sweat broke out over his brow.

He felt as if he had passed through a trial by fire, but Dominga seemed unaware of his struggle to regain his composure as she calmly poured the tea. However, by the time he came to take his cup from her she had surreptitiously corrected the neckline of her gown. Neither did she meet his eyes, lest he should read in her own what heady triumph she felt at succeeding in arousing him so easily.

Some time after they had drunk their tea and the tray had been removed, she allowed herself to yawn, then yawned again. She closed her book, scarcely one line of which she had actually read, and said: 'I believe I will retire, my lord.'

Hugo, who was sprawled in a chair some distance from her and had been thumbing through some old copies of

Quarterly Review, replied: 'As you wish. Ring for a servant if you're not sure of the way.'

'I think I can be depended upon to find my way to my own bed,' she retorted more pertly than she meant to, but she was piqued that he had not even afforded her the common courtesy of escorting her to the door and opening it for her. She let herself out and walked swiftly along the carpeted passages and up to her rooms.

Harris was waiting for her and since she had not been enlightened about what kind of a marriage this was, she took extra pains in preparing her mistress for the marriage bed.

Dominga was disrobed and clad in a nightgown of white silk and lace with a wispy, matching dressing-gown. Her hair was uncoiled, brushed and arranged over her shoulders and down her back in an apparently artless, natural way. Silk slippers with diamond-studded heels were put on her feet and then Harris, satisfied that no man—Earl or otherwise—could expect a more faultless bride, allowed herself to be dismissed.

She was not to know that after she had left Dominga cast off the robe and nightgown and clad herself anew in an equally pretty white set, but of an unmistakably different style. Then she sat down on the pink silk day-bed and waited.

Presently she heard what she was listening for, Hugo's footsteps. They passed her room and moved on. Dominga went quietly into her dressing-room and listened at the connecting door until she was sure the valet had performed all his bedtime tasks and gone away.

She waited a few minutes more then caught up the nightgown Harris had first selected and, holding a candle aloft, went through the connecting door into milord's dressing-room. All was darkness here, but as she went on into his bed-chamber she saw candles burning in the many-branched candelàbrum by the bed.

A lesser man than the Earl would have looked insignificant in the massive four-poster, which appeared to be a relic from the Middle Ages and could have accommodated Henry the Eighth and half his wives in relative comfort. Hugo, however, managed to dominate it, as he dominated most things, even though he only lounged against the pillows reading, a single cover apparently sufficient for him on this hot night.

His nightshirt was unfastened at the throat so that the candlelight gleamed on the firm flesh of his chest, and brightly highlighted the fair hair which fell across his forehead. Dominga's heart gave a strange lurch at the sight of him. The candle she held herself shook slightly and for one mad moment her resolution faltered. Then she remembered what had been her fate when she had allowed his physical power to overwhelm her once before, and she was able to glide forward to his bedside to carry out her mission.

Had she needed further armament against his attractiveness and her own weakness, the exultant light which kindled in his eyes when he saw her would have provided it, or the mocking smile which touched his lips when the thought flashed through his mind that only one thing could have brought her here . . . the wish to be his true wife, after all.

As she came within the full glow of the candles beside his bed she seemed to shimmer in a froth of white silk and lace, and all the desire Hugo had felt for her earlier returned as though he had never really mastered it.

What dark mysterious pools the candlelight made of her eyes, he thought, and how it emphasised the firm fullness of her lips. Hugo's need for her was too urgent to allow for any gloating remark on her submission, and he merely flicked aside the cover so that she might join him.

Dominga leaned across him, her hair brushing teasingly across his chest, and placed the nightgown she held in her hand in the space he had made for her. Then she straightened up, revelling in his confusion. 'That is the gown my maid dressed me in tonight. If it is found in your room tomorrow the servants will have no cause to chatter. Otherwise, the true state of affairs between us will be whispered all over the county by noon and, as your wife, I mean to protect your reputation as carefully as you promised to protect mine.'

Hugo was bereft of words. Dominga, smiling, curtsied and whether by accident or design a little hot grease from her candle dropped on that part of his chest which was bare. Pain jerked him out of his stupor and he grasped her wrist so tightly that she winced, exclaiming: 'Have a care, my lord!'

'You, madam, are the one who should have a care,' Hugo threatened softly. 'If you came here to torment me, you play a dangerous game.'

He flung her from him then and Dominga, although she staggered back, recovered quickly. 'I torment you?' she asked innocently. 'How could that be, when you swore it would take you all of a year to overcome your distaste of me?'

She turned and went back to her own apartment, sublimely sure that there was nothing the high and mighty Earl of Deversham desired more right then than his low-born Countess.

He was a long way from begging for her yet, but ultimately that lusty, unruly blood of his would ensure that he would have to possess her or go mad.

What heady wine revenge was, she thought, as she flung herself down on her bed more like an exuberant schoolgirl than a titled lady. She felt almost intoxicated as she blew out her bedside candles and lay back with her head on the soft pillows.

With one finger she traced the Deversham arms, surmounted by a 'D' and the whole enclosed in laurel leaves, embroidered on her pillowslip. Then, with a deep sigh of happiness which would have baffled Isabelle Yerberry and infuriated Désirée de Lafayeure, she closed her eyes and drifted into an untroubled sleep.

In his great bed, sleep eluded Hugo. Unsated desire caused him to turn this way and that as he roundly cursed his bride and all her unknown ancestors. Finally he tracked down the tantalising aura of perfume he thought she had left behind her to the nightgown which lay forgotten beside him.

With an oath he snatched it up and almost shredded it in fury before hurling it as far away from him as he could. It fell on to the carpet beyond the bed, where Stanton found it in the morning and was much impressed.

CHAPTER
THIRTEEN

HARRIS was miffed to be summoned to my lady's bed-chamber at first light the next morning. She had expected marriage to put an end to her mistress's eccentric habit of rising with the dawn to go riding, but Dominga wanted her hot chocolate and bread and butter as usual, and asked for the stables to be told she wanted her horse ready in half an hour.

Harris did not fail to notice that Dominga was wearing a different nightgown, although the Earl's fair head was not resting on the pillows beside his bride's. When, later, Stanton discreetly returned the other, tattered nightgown, Harris could only assume that the bridegroom was a passionate or impatient man, and probably both.

But Dominga showed no sign of being the worse for wear as Harris dressed her in a red velvet riding habit with dashing military-style epaulettes and buttons, and set a matching hat with a wickedly-curled feather at a saucy angle on her coiled hair.

Yet old habits die hard and as the new Countess was handed her gloves and riding crop, Harris commended her—as if she were still a maiden—to keep an eye on the weather and to hurry back if it looked like raining. Not that she feared her mistress would succumb to a chill, it was the velvet she was worried about.

None of the footmen who had hovered so diligently yesterday were to be seen at this early hour, but Dominga managed to find her way to the stables, which were already bustling with grooms. As she came out of one door on to the flagstones, Hugo came out of another, and they stopped in mutual surprise for each had imagined the other to be still safely asleep.

Dominga's heart gave a funny little tug as she saw that Hugo could look as dangerously attractive at dawn as he could at midnight. He was wearing the clothes which suited him best, riding breeches, top-boots and a long-tailed blue coat. Dark shadows under his eyes gave him a rather rakish look, but his face hardened when he saw his bride, looking ravishing in red velvet.

Not only had she robbed him of his night's sleep, she was about to spoil his favourite part of the day by thrusting her company upon him when he least wanted it. He made no attempt to disguise his annoyance, which angered Dominga because he had promised to keep up a pretence of cordiality between them for the servants' benefit.

The grooms were already looking at the Earl's thunderous expression with interest, so that Dominga was compelled to move forward and extend her hand to him. 'Well timed, my lord,' she said, as if they had arranged to meet this way.

Hugo had no choice but to bend over her hand and brush her fingers with reluctant lips. He straightened, glanced up at the clouds, and replied: 'The fine weather is breaking. Stanton, my valet, says we're in for a storm and he's seldom wrong. I advise you to cancel your ride.'

'Thank you for your concern, but I won't melt in a little rain,' Dominga replied sweetly, her smile scarcely disguising the fact that she was not going to give up her pleasure for the sake of his.

He glared at her, but the grooms were bringing up the horses. He tossed his bride, heavy as she was, up into her side-saddle, mounted his own horse and trotted out of the stable yard, leaving her to follow or not as she pleased.

She was appalled by his behaviour, but followed him with what good grace she could muster until he reined in and studied her thoroughbred mare closely. Melody had been brought down from Chersey by easy stages a few days earlier and she was decidedly frisky, but Hugo could not see her matching Sebastian's stride.

'You'll never keep up with me on that showy piece and I can't tolerate a sluggard's pace,' he said curtly. 'Stick to this wide path and I'll rejoin you in an hour or so on my way back.'

He galloped off before she could argue, but he was more at odds with himself than ever, so that he did not enjoy his ride across the quiet valley as much as usual. The precious sense of freedom was missing, for which he blamed his bride.

It wasn't apparent to him that he was behaving like an ill-mannered lout, for such had been his upbringing, with all his arrogance being encouraged rather than checked, that it simply never occurred to him to consider any viewpoint other than his own.

Hugo did not check Sebastian's pace until a distant rumble of thunder warned of the storm to come. He glanced back and reined in when he saw that his bride's horse, though some distance back, was gamely following.

When Dominga caught up with him her mare was far from blown but she herself was breathless. A wind had got up, whipping the flowing skirt of her velvet habit about her, but the flush on her cheeks was as much due to temper as the elements. 'By god, a peasant would not behave as badly as you do!' she exploded.

'Knowing nothing of peasants, madam, I must accept your word on that,' he replied with that high-bred insolence that always touched her to the raw.

Dominga drew in her breath but thunder growled again, and more closely, so that she cast an anxious look at the low clouds. 'We will have words another time,' she said grimly. 'My mare has a nervous disposition and doesn't care for violent storms. One of the faults of the over-bred, I gather. No doubt you suffer from a similar handicap yourself?'

'My greatest handicap is a wife who doesn't know when she isn't wanted,' he retorted.

'And mine is a husband who doesn't know how to behave in front of his own servants, let alone a lady.'

He leaned over and grabbed her bridle. 'By heaven, madam, you have a dangerous habit of pushing me too far.'

'Too far?' she repeated, her lip curling contemptuously. 'I haven't even started pushing you yet.' She brought her riding crop down savagely on his arm, causing him to swear and drop her bridle. Melody, already unsettled by the thunder, shied and skittered nervously as Dominga fought to bring her under control.

'A showy piece,' Hugo reaffirmed. 'You and your mare are well-matched.'

'Then so must you and I be,' Dominga snapped, 'for that is what you are, is it not? All show!' She turned Melody and raced back to Deversham Hall, as if trying to out-pace the large but occasional raindrops which began to fall.

Hugo followed more leisurely, but he caught up with her before long and they clattered into the stable yard together. Grooms who had been on the watch for them ran forward to grab their bridles. Hugo swung himself out of the saddle, jerked Dominga out of hers and set her on her feet with precious little ceremony.

The rain, which had been teasing the parched earth after such a long spell of fine weather, now came down with sufficient force to slap stingingly against the flagstones and bounce some inches up again.

Dominga put down her head and ran for the house. She tripped on her long skirt and would have fallen had not Hugo grabbed her arm and held her up as they raced on together. His fingers gripped her soft flesh tightly, becoming more painful by the second, so that she realised he was paying her back for lashing out at him with her riding crop.

The moment they were inside the door she pulled her arm free of his grasp. He laughed and said: 'So you don't care for your own medicine? But I mustn't mock you for you look a sorry enough sight as it is, and it will distress you to know that your habit doesn't look half so gaudy now that it is wet.'

'Gaudy!' Dominga gasped, knowing her taste was above question and that nobody could wear red as well as she. 'If that is what you think, I can only commiserate with you, my lord. What poor little squabs of women you must have been accustomed to up till now!'

She left him and went fuming up to her rooms, her riding crop beating ominously against her leg. Nothing could have been clearer to her than that bringing Hugo to heel was going to be a harder task than she had supposed. He was fighting back, and in none too gentlemanly a manner, as if he were as set on crushing her as she was on crushing him.

Well, she raged inwardly, there would be all the more triumph in vanquishing a worthy opponent. She should be grateful that Hugo was the twin who had survived, for she doubted if Harry would have given her half the sport. And the final outcome could not really be in any doubt, for no matter how long the struggle for ascendancy between herself and her husband should prove to be, she was the one with the stamina and motivation to sustain it. She had proved that already by getting this far along the road to her revenge.

She scarcely listened to Harris's recriminations as the velvet habit was stripped from her and put tenderly aside to be restored to its former glory later, but snapped: 'Never mind that now. Bring me my *gaudiest* morning dress!'

'There is nothing of that description in your wardrobe,' Harris replied, looking at her mistress as if she had run mad.

'My brightest one, then,' Dominga ordered impatiently. She would rather go down to breakfast stark naked than sombrely clad, otherwise Hugo might think she had toned down her appearance because of what he had said.

The gown Harris fetched was of buttercup muslin with tiny green rosettes sewn on to the scalloped frills at the hem and neck. Dominga frowned at the rosettes. 'Didn't I ask for them to be replaced?'

'Yes, my lady, but you haven't yet decided what you want them replaced with. Shall I fetch another gown?'

'No, no. It will have to do as it is.'

Harris raised her eyebrows, for Dominga was normally fussy in the extreme over her appearance, but she wasn't to know that the Countess didn't trust the Earl to delay his breakfast to suit her convenience.

The footman who had been sent by Jamieson to conduct the Countess to the breakfast parlour, blinked when he saw her and thought that she looked like a walking ray of sunshine, which indeed she did.

From the ribbon threaded through her dusky locks to her dainty feet she was all yellow, save for the green rosettes which she no longer lamented because, if not precisely gaudy, were certainly bright enough to offend the Earl if red velvet was too much for him. With any luck, she thought maliciously, her appearance might quite spoil his meal. Unfortunately, however, she was unable to judge what kind of impact she made on him for her arrival in the breakfast-room coincided with the table being reset.

It was a cosy room with an informal atmosphere, due mostly to the table being of a more intimate size than the one in the small dining-room. But Hugo, finding that Jamieson had rather romantically set the Countess's place next to his own, had pithily ordered her place to be removed to the foot of the table.

He'd had the grace to remind Jamieson, after their eyes had met for a split-second, that he liked to read the newspapers at the breakfast table, and how the deuce could he do that with the Countess almost sat in his lap?

Dominga waited quietly while the table was rearranged, but inwardly she burned with humiliation and wondered if Hugo was deliberately supplying the servants with items of gossip to tattle about behind her back.

When Jamieson stood back and bowed her into her chair, she sat down gracefully. 'How thoughtful of you, Hugo. I hate to be cramped at the table,' she said, then turned her attention to the butler. 'It was arranged for my journals to be delivered to the nearest receiving house to the Hall from today. Have they arrived? They should have been brought up with the Earl's.'

Jamieson bowed again and said that the papers had arrived, so that Dominga favoured him with her sweetest smile and asked for them to be brought to her. When this was done, the butler was treated to the bemusing spectacle of the Earl and Countess separately engrossed in their journals as if they had been wed twenty-four years instead of twenty-four hours.

When the young couple had been served with all they wished, Jamieson signalled to his supporting footman and they withdrew. Dominga deliberately went on reading the announcement of her marriage in the *Morning Post* and only when she had finished did she look coldly at her husband and say: 'For all your grand titles and ancient lineage, Hugo, I am beginning to think you are a pathetic and rather poor sort of man. You promised to uphold my position as your wife and yet you demean me before the servants on every possible occasion. This—' she waved her hand disdainfully towards her place setting—'was an unnecessary piece of spite. You will pay for it by conducting me over the house yourself this morning, so that just for once your behaviour will be precisely what your servants and I might reasonably expect.'

Hugo threw down his newspaper and stood up, his face quite white. 'You dare to tell me what to do in my own house!'

'It is my house also now and I have no intention of being treated in it as if I am of no more importance than a menial.' Dominga paused, then went on deliberately: 'If it is war you want, Hugo, you can have it. Either you will behave correctly towards me or I shall quarrel with you on all those occasions when you do not—regardless of whose sight or hearing we may be in. I'd rather the world knew me as a shrew than an unwanted wife.'

'You,' he reminded her through clenched teeth, 'chose to be no proper wife.'

'I stated my reason, which you accepted with alacrity rather than reluctance. One thing is sure, Hugo, you would never make a martyr—you recant too often.'

His fists clenched. 'Have a care what you are saying, madam, or you'll choke on your own words.'

'Oh, don't go all gothic on me because I won't murmur yes and amen to everything you say,' Dominga advised him shortly. 'Did you expect me to be over-awed by marrying an Earl? I, who purchased my coronet just as I would purchase anything else I fancied?'

For a moment she thought she had taunted him too much for his eyes chilled to chips of blue ice, but he merely said scornfully: 'I didn't think it would be long before you were thrusting your fortune down my throat again.'

'And why not, since you are forever thrusting your abominable breeding down mine,' Dominga retorted. 'My money, Hugo, is one of those things you will have to learn to live with, just as I have to learn to live with your arrogance and conceit.'

'Poor little Cit's daughter, is that what hurts so much?' he asked mockingly. 'Because you have nothing to be arrogant about? Well, I may be a purchased Earl but I am no tame one. You will never rule here in my place, and if you wish to live at peace with me then keep out of my way.'

'Oh, don't be so childish,' Dominga snapped. 'Such a fuss and bother you make about what should be a simple understanding between us. Pray don't tell me that I go too far again, either, or I will set up such a screech that your worshipful servants will think you are murdering me.'

'An idea, madam, that has more than once crossed my mind,' Hugo responded.

Unexpectedly, Dominga laughed. 'Not before I've had my London season, please!'

But Hugo's face remained as thunderous as ever. 'I'm glad you see some humour in our situation, for it escapes me,' he answered broodingly.

Dominga eyed him carefully and decided it was time to change tactics. Having stung him to the raw, she would now apply salve to his wounded sensibilities. She smiled at him, allowing her dimples to show and her eyes to soften before saying with the devastating charm which she hoped would ultimately be his undoing: 'Poor Hugo. An unwanted Earldom thrust on you—and then me. I do sympathise with you, I promise, but I'm sure we can get on together a great deal better if only you'll co-operate a tiny bit.'

Her smile was beguiling, as it was supposed to be, but Hugo studied her warily. Privileged by birth he might be, but he was no nincompoop and it seemed to him that any woman who could be a veritable virago one moment and as soft as a dove the next was playing a devilishly deep game. He distrusted her sweet smile, instinctively feeling he was being drawn into a trap, although he could not imagine what it might be.

The only thing he was sure of was that he'd had enough of bickering, so he said decisively: 'I will tell you the exact extent to which I am willing to co-operate, as you call it, with you. We will ride out in the mornings and take breakfast together. Then we will go our separate ways until dinner, when we will spend the evenings together. That should be sufficient to stop any whispers, and therefore sustain your precious dignity, for nobody will expect us to live in each other's pockets. I don't know how things are managed in the merchant class, but that is general practice in mine.'

Dominga was not used to her charm failing, nor had she expected Hugo to put her in her place as effectively as he had after he had seduced her two years ago. She was filled afresh with rage and chagrin and for one wild moment she felt like leaping at him and shredding his aristocratic countenance with her nails.

'Well, madam?' he asked.

His dispassionate voice douched her fiery emotions as effectively as if he'd thrown cold water into her face. It also brought home to her the skill with which he could rob her of the initiative. Instead of her dictating terms to him, she had been dictated to, and she didn't like it one little bit.

But she wasn't her father's daughter for nothing, and if she had to retreat it was going to be in good order. 'What you say sounds reasonable,' she replied, 'although I must insist that this, the first day of our marriage, be counted as an exception. I will *not* have the housekeeper show me over my new home. You will do it, as a bridegroom should.'

He bowed, perfectly prepared to do his duty today to gain his freedom tomorrow, and spent the rest of the day conducting his bride over Deversham Hall with that polite indifference at which he excelled, and which she found so infuriating. For he had her measure now, being perceptive enough to realise she loathed this treatment more than anything else.

Dominga was, indeed, seething and she retaliated by lingering longer than necessary in unimportant apartments worth no more than a cursory glance, and by asking him so many questions that he felt like a walking guide-book.

She tried alternately to goad and charm him out of his soulless civility, but with no success. He remained aloof, playing the role of bored but polite husband to such perfection that she could willingly have boxed his ears.

Had she but known it, Hugo came very close to cracking in the picture gallery when she required a potted history, right back to when they had been mere barons, of all those Huntsleighs whose likenesses hung there. It was only with superhuman restraint that he complied, instead of telling her not to dawdle so over a bunch of dusty old bores.

When she came back for a second time to stand before the portraits of himself and Harry, he almost uttered aloud one or two of the barrack-room oaths with which he had been privately relieving his feelings for some time.

The truth was that, even though he was aware of his own

irrationality, he still could not see his bride as anything but an intruder here. He could not think of her as a Huntsleigh at all, and was therefore reluctant to share any part of his possessions or his past with her. He just did not, could not, feel married and he didn't think the fact that he hadn't slept with her had much to do with it. No, the only tie by which she held him—could ever hold him, he was sure—was a legal one.

He looked at her in all her buttercup brightness, appreciated her earthy attraction, but knew he could never be anchored by lust alone. His rebellious heart still cried out for Désirée, still rejected Dominga as a substitute. He gloomily supposed that he was doomed to be forever torn in two, swaying towards his duty one moment and his desires the next. And he wondered if his duty could ever be more onerous than this, since it had him standing immobile for several minutes while Dominga studied the portraits of himself and his brother with extraordinary closeness.

Hugo was depicted in all the glory of his Hussar uniform and Dominga was woman enough to feel that funny little tug at her heart again, and to wonder how she would feel about him if she had met him this summer for the first time instead of two years ago. Then his portrait blurred before her eyes, and she saw again the patchwork quilt and the toss of the coins, heard the creak of the bed as Hugo replaced his brother, felt again his powerful arms around her.

She remembered, would always remember, every detail of that day and she brought herself deliberately back to the present by observing: 'You are the image of each other.'

'Scarcely an original observation,' Hugo pointed out.

'But still relevant, surely?' Dominga countered.

He predicted: 'Next you will observe, as everybody does, the only noticeable difference between Harry and myself. His eyes were grey. Mine are blue.'

'Ah, yes, I hadn't missed that, I can assure you.'

Hugo frowned. There was an enigmatic quality in her voice which puzzled him, but he did not question her for she was at last moving on.

The picture gallery completed their tour of the inhabited wing of the house and they went down to the small dining-room for a cold luncheon, where the epergne bedecked with fresh flowers and fruit once more cut off communication between them.

The afternoon was spent exploring the older wings of the Hall, which Hugo had not seen himself since he and Harry had played in them as boys. He thought wistfully how happy and uncomplicated those days had been, but Dominga was concerned with more practical matters.

Her gown grew dusty as they roamed these neglected regions and she privately resolved that fresh air and polish would be known here again. To her mind, the care that was lavished on the inhabited wing of the house was like keeping the maindeck of a ship in pristine condition while the keel was left to rot unnoticed. It was all too obvious that for generations the Earls had been careless of this part of their history, but it was also her history now, and it would be preserved.

Hugo half-expected her to be drooping with weariness at dinner, but her vitality was undimmed as she joined him wearing a gown of diaphanous gauze over a green silk underdress. She was normally very sparing with jewellery, but tonight diamonds sparkled at her ears, throat and wrists. It was her little way of reminding him who had the true buying power here, which served him right after the set-down he had given her that morning, she thought.

After dinner, Hugo set up a card table since he was damned if he was going to spend another intolerably dull evening leafing through out-of-date magazines. Besides, cards might just be able to distract his attention from the way his bride's shimmering gown enhanced the curves of her body.

They played piquet and various other games which did not require more than two people, and Hugo found Dominga such an able foe that when they left the card table the honours were evenly divided between them a circumstance which wrung from him his first real respect for her.

Désirée had no head for cards and although she looked delightfully pretty as she hesitated over which card to play, she was a frustrating partner or opponent for a skilled player like Hugo. Dominga, on the other hand, had a good memory for numbers and she played with flair and confidence. This ensured that Hugo went off the bed stimulated rather than bored, though not for the life of him would he have acknowledged, even to himself, that there might be some occasions on which Dominga's company might be preferable to Désirée's.

It was a pity Dominga didn't know she had taken her first tiny chip out of the pedestal Hugo had erected for Désirée in his mind, or she might have left him in peace. As it was, she succumbed to her own particular devil and made another sortie into his bed-chamber after the servants had retired for the night.

This time she left no perfumed nightgown behind her to taunt him but, after hovering long enough within the light of his candelabrum for him to take in once more the full glory of her in scanty nightclothes and with hair unbound, she contented herself with leaving one of her diamond-heeled slippers on the floor.

But Hugo was no Prince Charming to fondle the slipper and sigh after its owner, and his feelings as he resigned himself to another restless night bordered more on what savage satisfaction it would give him to drive that dainty diamond heel through his tormenting bride's heart.

CHAPTER
FOURTEEN

THERE was no mention of torment or slippers between the bridal pair as they rode out together the next morning in blustery but bright weather, nor did they touch on any subject that might have caused controversy between them. Each was grimly determined not to be the first to break the pact between them, and thereby giving the other the chance to crow.

After breakfast, Hugo went off to look at some labourers' dilapidated cottages, leaving Dominga to amuse herself. She was nothing loath since she had plenty to keep her busy. Her first task was to write a note to Mr Ponting, enclosing a draft upon her bank which would drive from his mind all memory of the uncomfortable time he had had while performing his part in bringing the marriage about. She did not ask for an account of his expenses but added an extra fifty guineas to the five hundred agreed upon, which was to be her last act of unqualified generosity over her purchase of the Earl.

Thereafter she watched pennies, just as her father had taught her to do. The world, he had often said, was divided into two types of people, those who got plucked and those who did the plucking. Save a shilling out of every guinea you have to spend, he had counselled her, and you won't be one of those who end up without a feather to fly with. So although she spent many guineas over the following weeks, Dominga contrived to save more than a few shillings. Without precisely haggling with tradesmen over goods she ordered, she managed to drive a harder bargain than ever the housekeeper or the steward would have, and they prided themselves on their thrift.

Moreover, the new Countess proved to be a powerhouse of energy, impossible to thwart or side-track. Nobody was left in any doubt that, although only seventeen, she knew what she wanted and how to get it.

During her first week at Deversham Hall there seemed scarcely a servant who wasn't involved in compiling some list or other, for Dominga initiated a gigantic stocktaking as if she'd taken over the management of a business rather than the running of an aristocrat's principal residence.

She called for all the linen in the house to be listed, with the condition of each item noted, and the same applied to china, cutlery, cooking utensils, furniture in need of repair, and so on. This was because her sharp eyes had noticed that although the Hall was manned by sufficient servants to uphold the Earl's dignity, straitened circumstances had led to economies in many areas which did not affect his immediate comfort.

When the lists were completed they revealed that there was scarcely a sheet in the house undarned, not a set of crockery that was complete, and that the attics were groaning under furniture which needed only a carpenter's or upholsterer's care to restore it to full use. Mrs Chandler was torn between gratification at having these matters attended to and dismay that the Countess refused to order new stock from those warehouses which the Family had patronised in better times. She was not to know that although a fair proportion of the Countess's fortune was respectably invested in Funds, she also had direct interests in mills, potteries, haulage companies and many other businesses of a kind that aristocrats disdained to sully their hands with.

Naturally Dominga took advantage of her business connections wherever possible, so that a high proportion of the goods she ordered were bought at a discount, which gave Mrs Chandler the gravest misgivings until she saw that everything which came into the Hall was of the finest quality.

The new linen was sent out to local seamstresses to be embroidered with the Deversham crest; carpenters and all manner of craftsmen were brought in to repair and restore the older wings of the house to their former glory.

Amid all this bustle, an account in the journals of the wedding between Augustus Marsham and Désirée de Lafayeure did not go unnoticed by the Earl or his Countess.

Hugo's moodiness, which had been on the wane since Dominga had proved herself a woman of her word by bothering him hardly at all providing he kept his side of their pact, returned with a vengeance. The supposition that he was on his own honeymoon had saved him from having to attend the ceremony, but visions of Désirée lying in Marsham's arms drove him half-demented. He threw himself into the reorganisation of his lands more grimly than ever, so that between himself and his bride there was scarcely a corner of the Deversham domain, within the house or without, that was left untouched.

Hugo bought new cattle to revitalise run-down herds, and meadows which had been untouched for years came under the scythe to provide winter hay. He had rotting sties at the home farm demolished, new ones built, and reintroduced pigs for the first time since his grandfather's day. Repairs were carried out on those labourers' cottages that were worth saving, otherwise they were also demolished and rebuilt.

The benefits brought to his land and his dependants by his marriage were felt everywhere, and the Earl would have been a very odd character indeed had he not felt a glow of pride at all he was achieving. And it was because he had involved himself personally, instead of leaving the reorganisation to hirelings, that he began to get over Désirée's marriage.

He was too young and volatile to mope for ever and the next project he undertook—buying brood mares and a suitable stallion to raise hunters for his own use and for sale—was so close to his heart that he showed every sign of recovering those high spirits which had been his before Harry's death had so dramatically altered his life.

Even Dominga felt the benefit of his returning good humour. As the weeks passed and she became an established part of his life, it was impossible for him to continue to regard her as an intruder. And his sense of fair play, which had always been a integral part of his character, could not be ignored any longer. The more he observed his bride, the more he had to admit to himself that his gibes at her lack of breeding had been unfounded.

It still chafed his pride, and always would, that he had

been forced to make a beggar-marriage, but he was no longer so wrapped up in his own troubles that he couldn't see that everybody else—from his servants to his neighbours—approved of the new Countess of Deversham. She got her own way in all things, certainly, but such was the charm she could radiate when it suited her that nobody bore her any grudge. She showed every sign of not only being a suitable countess but also a magnificent one, which could only add to Hugo's esteem. On a more personal note he was becoming increasingly preoccupied in wondering whether she would be equally magnificent in bed—when he finally got her there.

He slipped unconsciously into using her name instead of the contemptuous 'madam', a circumstance which caused Dominga to smile and feel she was slipping under his guard and into his affections at last.

And so she was, although Hugo's reappraisal of her did not take place in sudden, blinding enlightenments as if blinkers had been lifted from his eyes and his deep prejudices torn from his soul. Rather, it was a gradual process of learning to live with the inevitable and finding it not half so grim as he had feared.

If he had married Isabelle Yerberry, comparison between her and Désirée would have daily increased his loyalty to his first love. Dominga, however, was never dull and hers was such a vital personality that it was inevitable the absent Désirée should cease to dominate Hugo's thoughts, if not his affections.

He even came to appreciate Dominga's frequently caustic tongue and to be amused rather than annoyed by it, though it meant their life together was stimulating rather than serene. They came to know the best and the worst of each other, for although Dominga was mostly beguiling, there were times when something Hugo said or did provoked her into giving him such a pithy reading of his character that he responded equally vitriolically in his own defence.

The servants would shudder at these times, and Deversham Hall would once more seem too small to hold the pair of them, but these stormy scenes would pass and they would settle down again to become, if not the best of friends, at least the best of enemies.

Gradually they became less rigid about the terms of the pact they had made until they were as much in each other's company as out of it. This began when members of the neighbouring gentry began to pay morning calls and civility obliged Hugo to accompany his wife when she returned the calls.

He found he had much to talk to his bride about when they were in the chaise going to, or returning from, one of these courtesy visits. The first real bridge of communication between them was provided by their mutual interest in the revitalisation of the Deversham estates, and soon their conversation extended to horses, local items of gossip and whether or not they liked the way the mutton was dressed at last night's dinner.

Both were naturally gregarious and hated to be doing nothing, so they accepted most of the invitations which came their way until the local social scene was revolving around the dashing young Earl and his charming bride.

Their company was sought after by aspiring hostesses not only because they were titled, but because they were fun. Hugo could be counted on to dance with all the pretty girls, and sometimes even the plain ones, too, while his Countess inspired sighs and sonnets from the young men and rusty gallantry from their fathers.

Country ladies were great letter writers, and not above exaggeration, and so the news that Hugo was no longer to be pitied because he had married for love as well as money began to spread through polite society. It was true, they wrote, that the Earl and Countess did not exactly hang on each other's arms—which would have been shockingly underbred, anyway!—but the frequency with which they were seen in each other's company revealed that there was a very close bond between them.

Dominga would have smiled at this description of her relationship with Hugo, and he would have laughed out loud, but there was no doubt that he missed her when business compelled her to go up to London for a couple of days. Not that they were even talking to each other when she set out, for they had had a right royal row over her commercial interests.

Hugo had ordered her to have nothing to do with 'Cits' dealings' and to sell out, respectably reinvesting her money in land and Funds. She had refused, and travelled up to Town with Hugo's parting prediction that she would soon have a new title—that of The Merchant Countess.

She did not need her husband's contempt to warn her to be discreet in her business dealings, and if she increased her interest in the East India trade by becoming co-owner of another cutter, nobody in the *ton* was any the wiser. She worked, as her father had bid her, through diverse agents whom he had trusted.

Her two days in London extended to four, partly to set in motion some alterations to Deversham House and partly to indulge in a shopping spree until she felt tranquil enough to face her autocratic husband again.

If he had called her many names, she had also called him quite a few, of which 'despot' had lingered longest in his mind. When she returned to the Hall he greeted her with frigid politeness, but she was at her most bewitching and he had missed her abrasive company too much to sulk for long.

Besides, it was good to have dinner with her again. Some time previously, when he had been feeling particularly well disposed towards his bride, Hugo had had the wretched epergne removed to a sideboard and a leaf taken out of the table so that they could continue a conversation they had begun in the Crimson Saloon. This cosier state still existed and tonight Dominga was at her sunniest best as she strove to worm her way back into his good graces. Her dimples were very much in evidence, her eyelashes fluttered, her conversation sparkled and she fell into one artless pose after another for his benefit.

What was more, after dinner she let him thrash her at cards, looking adorably rueful as she lost one game after another. At last she exclaimed with well-feigned exasperation that he was too good for her tonight, and she would play no more.

She was wearing a white silk gown decorated with ribbons of her favourite scarlet, and as he came round the table to hold her chair back for her, she deliberately brushed against him when she stood up. It was a clever move, for her gown seemed to slip naturally from one shoulder, which was quite her favourite trick.

Hugo gazed for long seconds at her bare flesh, calmly adjusted her gown to its correct position, then looked into her eyes with a wicked light in his own. 'You really must change your dressmaker, Dominga, for none of your gowns appears to fit you properly. What are you doing, buying them at a discount?'

'No, I am not,' she snapped, as angry at herself as him, for she didn't need it spelled out to her that Hugo had seen through her role of innocent seductress.

'Then perhaps you could have your gowns adjusted before the Season starts. Nobody appears half-naked at *ton* parties unless it is deliberately so. It leads to too much of this—' And he deliberately exposed her shoulder again and bent down to kiss her bare shoulder.

Such a sweet sensation shot through Dominga that she couldn't have answered even if she could have thought of something to say. This was what she had worked for, plotted for, since her marriage, but now that it was happening she felt something more like anguish than triumph. Moreover, rather than capitalising on her success, she blushed like a schoolgirl.

Hugo straightened, replaced her gown once more, then took her face between his hands and asked softly: 'Why do you play with me, Dominga?'

She was thrown into total confusion for his hands felt tender as they cradled her face and the warmth in his eyes seemed, for once, divorced of lust. She had the crazy feeling that she was with a stranger, somebody she couldn't even begin to recognise, and she wished desperately that he would make one of his cutting remarks so that she could know him once more.

He outlined her lips with one light finger and asked again: 'Why? Why extract a promise from me not to touch you for a year, then do your best to tease me into breaking my word? Is it just the woman in you awakening? I tell myself that that is all it is, and yet I can never be quite sure. But whatever the reason, you must either release me from my promise or help me keep it.'

She was unable to bear the softness in his eyes and voice any longer and she looked down, her long eyelashes casting

shadows on her cheeks which were deathly white now that
her flushes had drained away. She felt disorientated. It was
as if the man had stepped out from behind the Earl and she
saw him as a human being for the first time since he had
seduced her, rather than the mere object of her revenge.

She didn't know why she should be so shattered by his
tenderness, except that she had never expected it, and she
was filled with the bewilderment of a person who has taken
a wrong turning somewhere and can't get a familiar bearing.

She began to tremble, which made her feel as much of a
stranger to herself as Hugo was to her, but it caused Hugo
to release her instantly and say: 'Run along to bed now. I
didn't mean to frighten you, not to scold, but neither do I
want you to be burnt in a fire of your own making. You are
so young and lovely and I'm—' he smiled at her in a way
that made her treacherous heart turn over—'well, I'm no
saint.'

Dominga fled. She was still deathly pale when she
reached her rooms and her brown eyes were wide and
disbelieving, as if she had seen an apparition which, in a
way, she had. Her reeling senses told her she had seen the
man she might have loved, had she not seen the side of him
she hated first.

'Whatever's the matter, my lady?' Harris exclaimed,
unused to Dominga being in anything but full control of
herself.

'Nothing. I have—I have the headache,' Dominga replied.

She lied, and Harris knew it, for Dominga had never
suffered from such a thing in her life. She thought her
mistress must have had another tiff with her husband, and
come off the worse, so she changed her for bed as quickly as
possible, knowing that she would arise in the morning fit
and ready for another encounter which she would win.

After Harris had replaced the jewellery Dominga had
been wearing in its velvet-lined box, she was surprised
when Dominga said: 'Leave that where it is, and the key. I
will put it away later. That will be all for tonight, thank
you.'

Harris had no choice but to curtsy and withdraw,

although she began to think that something more serious than a tiff had occurred between the Earl and Countess, which was a pity when they were beginning to get on so well.

The weather was cold now, but there was a warm fire burning in Dominga's bedroom and as soon as Harris was gone she carried the jewellery box over to it, placing it on the thick carpet and kneeling before it.

She pulled her quilted gown more tightly about her, then carefully lifted out the partitioned upper layer to reveal the less-favoured jewels reposing beneath. Among them were two silk purses. One contained a small fortune in uncut jewels which her father had purchased when he'd feared the war with France might affect English currency, and the other contained the ten golden guineas which Hugo had showered on her—so generously, as he had thought.

This was the purse Dominga lifted out. She undid the tie-string and spilled the guineas into her lap but her hand was shaking so that some rolled over the carpet.

She gathered them together and stared at them as if they were the signpost she needed to find her way back to familiar ground. She remained there until the flames disappeared from the fire, until the coals lost their glow and began to collapse into embers.

But by that time her brain had regained mastery over her emotions and she thought she had the answer to Hugo's inexplicable behaviour. He had seen through her, realised that she was trying to make him fall in love with her, although he couldn't know why and so had probably put it down to feminine vanity. And, being Hugo, he was paying her back trick for trick. He was still trying to gain mastery over her, but this time by making her fall in love with *him*!

She had found ways through his armour and tonight had been his first attempt to find ways through hers. Her cheeks burned again as she considered what a fillip it would have been to his vanity had she, in the fleeting confusion of her emotions caused by his surprise change of tactics, capitulated.

The more she thought about it, the more convinced Dominga became that it wasn't her body alone that he wanted but her love. She had been naïve to imagine that a man like Hugo could be content with anything less. He was a neck-or-nothing man at all things, so naturally he would want to exert his precious superiority over his wife in every possible way.

The Dominga that went to bed that night wasn't precisely harder than the one that had arisen from it that morning, but she was sure she was a great deal wiser. Even so, she made no sortie into the Earl's bed-chamber to leave an intimate item of her clothing behind. For the first time ever, she did not dare. She was prepared for the Earl to try to turn the tables on her again, but she was not going to risk such a thing happening anywhere near his great bed . . .

There was nothing in Dominga's demeanour the next day to suggest she had been up half the night searching her soul, but Hugo's behaviour towards her was never quite the same again. He treated her with what she would have termed affection had she not known it to be false, and when he willingly fetched and carried for her she eyed him warily.

It was certainly a novel experience to be courted by her proud husband, and as the days passed she learned how dangerously charming he could be, but she wished he would storm and rage at her again. It was a case of the devil she knew being better than the one she didn't.

Towards the end of October Hugo, who had shown remarkable tolerance towards the knocking and hammering that had been going on in the older wings of the house, declared that he had had enough when painters moved in to make his immediate living quarters uncomfortable. He ordered his bride to pack her bags, saying that they would go up to his hunting box in Leicestershire until peace had returned to Deversham Hall.

They were off the next day since Dominga was one of those rare women who could undertake a long journey with a masculine lack of fuss. They took only Harris, Stanton, Jamieson and the groom Parsons with them because the hunting box had a resident couple as caretakers, and any other help that was necessary could be hired locally.

They stayed a month, the Earl and Countess joining two hunts, where Dominga was an immediate hit with Hugo's friends and neighbours not only for her wit and beauty but because she could stay in the saddle all day without complaining.

The hunting box could be described as snug, since it had only ten bedrooms, but Dominga found plenty to do there and launched into a new programme of repair and redecoration. When the hammering and sawing began afresh, Hugo moved his bride over the border into Lincolnshire to spend a fortnight with a cousin, before returning to Deversham Hall for Christmas. In the New Year they set out, regardless of the awful state of the roads, for Somerset to stay with yet another of Hugo's cousins. There they remained until March, returning home as spring brought new life to the lovely valley the Hall was set in.

Harris busied herself in Dominga's suite, now stark white with hangings and upholstery of scarlet, for all the Countess's clothes had to be overhauled for the Season. Most of the household would be travelling up to London in mid-April, so Dominga also found herself with plenty to organise. This she did in her usual brisk fashion so that by the third week in March she was impatient to be packed and be gone.

In Paris at this time a great deal of packing was already going on. Mrs Désirée Marsham, who had been the toast of Paris since her husband had carried her off there after their marriage, had told her husband she no longer wished to travel on to Italy in the spring as they had planned.

The fact was that correspondence from her friends in England had marred what would otherwise have been a most satisfactory honeymoon. She was as pampered and cosseted a bride as she could have wished, and her adoring Augustus had lavished all manner of expensive gifts on her, from diamonds to set off her fair beauty to a carriage lined in silk the precise blue of her eyes.

Since before Christmas, however, letters to Désirée had hinted that Hugo's marriage had been as much a love-match as a matter of financial convenience. Through later letters she had been able to follow Hugo and Dominga's giddy whirl about the country, and her lovely face hardened when she read that they were rarely seen out of each other's company.

There seemed no doubt, either, since she heard it from so

many sources, that the Countess was as lovely as Major Millichip had originally described.

Désirée knew that her own marriage was an ideal one for her—certainly Hugo would never have made such an easy-going and open-handed husband as Augustus—and yet she had clung to the hope that Hugo was mismatched, for that was the only way she could be sure he would remain hers.

What Désirée had she held, and Hugo she still regarded as hers. Such store did she set by her own beauty, which had so far brought her everything she wanted, that she could brook no rival. She would see this Dominga woman for herself, and outshine her. Then she would crook her little finger at Hugo and he would come running, as all men did when she showed them favour.

But first she must get back to England, and a letter from her mother saying she was staying with friends just outside Portsmouth gave her the opportunity she was seeking. Portsmouth was in Hampshire and according to her latest letters Hugo and his wife were again in residence at Deversham Hall, which was in the same county.

She developed, therefore, a desire to see her mother which was greater, she persuaded her husband, than her wish to see Italy. Not that Augustus needed much persuading for he was one of those English gentlemen who could never be quite easy in foreign company, although he would willingly have travelled to Outer Mongolia if that was what Désirée wanted.

Thus it was that within a few days a very surprised Comtesse de Lafayeure was being hugged by her daughter and hearing rather bemusedly how much she had been missed. She was suspicious, as only a mother who knows her daughter inside out can be, and when within another few days Désirée announced her intention of travelling on to London to refurbish her wardrobe for the Season, the Comtesse spoke her mind.

'Do you mean to travel by way of Deversham Hall?' she demanded.

Désirée smiled in a coquettish way that cut no ice with her mother. 'Perhaps,' she admitted.

'It won't do!' the Comtesse snapped. 'It's much too soon Do your duty by Marsham first, you fool. You have so much now—why throw it away for a man who will still be eager for you in two or three years' time?'

A mulish look came into Désirée's eyes. 'I've heard Hugo is—is fond of his wife,' she replied, since she could not bring herself to go further than that.

'What you've heard,' her mother deduced, 'is that she is a beauty. So have I, but tell me any woman of fortune who has been described as anything else. Have patience, my child. Do not spoil what you have already for Hugo's sake. He will always be yours.'

'If I discover that what you say is true then I will leave well alone,' Désirée replied. 'If not—well, we will see.'

'Indeed we will,' the Comtesse retorted bitterly. 'Do you suppose that Marsham is a fool?'

'Yes,' her daughter replied deliberately. 'Kind, generous, worthy—but undoubtedly a fool. Have no fear on that score, Mama, for dear Augustus will always believe whatever I choose to tell him.'

'I hope you may be right,' the Comtesse retorted. 'Because you are married now you believe you know all about men. *Mon dieu!* You are a novice. When you get to my age, then, perhaps, you will know men. Stay away from Deversham Hall. I do not fear for you from Hugo, but his Countess—I hear she is equal to anything and anybody!'

Désirée smiled and patted her mother's cheek. 'You grow timid with age, Mama,' she chided. 'But me, I am also equal to anything!'

She truly believed she was, too, when she was in the chaise with Augustus by her side and Portsmouth was fading behind them. After not too many miles had passed, she began to groan and cover her eyes.

Augustus was all concern. 'What is it, dearest?' he enquired in alarm, piling more travelling blankets about her because he distrusted an English spring almost as much as he distrusted foreigners.

'Do not be cross with me, dearest Augustus,' she replied faintly, 'but I fear one of my migraines is coming on.'

He patted her hands and kissed her pale cheek. 'We will stop at the nearest inn so that you might rest,' he promised.

'Not an inn,' she moaned. 'I feel too ill to rest among

strangers. Can we be close to a house where I might recover among friends?'

Augustus promptly rapped on the carriage roof to gain the attention of his coachman. Learning from that worthy man that the nearest house of respectable repute was Deversham Hall, Augustus's brow lost its worried frown and he directed that they be conveyed there immediately.

The Earl and the Countess of Deversham were having an amicable lunch when the news was brought to them that Mr and Mrs Augustus Marsham were at the door.

Hugo froze, and Dominga's eyes settled thoughtfully on him although she said nothing. She rose from the table with him and together they went into the entrance hall where Augustus stood with his wife.

Désirée, muffled in sables, showed no signs of the invalid. Her fair ringlets peeped out from her fetching bonnet and her blue eyes burned with a fever that had nothing to do with sickness as they settled on Hugo.

Having reassured herself he was precisely as she had last seen him, her eyes travelled on to Dominga, and she suffered a shock.

A tall woman with curves which made Désirée's seem insignificant looked down on her. Dark-eyed magnificence was offered in challenge to her own fair etherealness. They were at opposite ends of the pole, Désirée and Dominga, and they knew it. What was more to the point as blue eyes met brown, they knew each other as enemies.

CHAPTER
FIFTEEN

THERE were two people in the Deversham household who, regardless of Dominga's little ploys, suspected that the Earl and Countess were play-acting rather than performing certain important marriage duties. No matter how many nightgowns and slippers might be found in my lord's bed-chamber, Stanton and Harris had not failed to notice the lack of intimacy between the young couple.

Stanton's loyalty and Harris's discretion made them quite unable to discuss their doubts, but each came to understand that the other was an ally in keeping the true state of affairs from the rest of the servants.

Below-stairs gossip had put Harris in full possession of the facts regarding the Earl's thwarted love for Mrs Désirée Marsham, so when that lady arrived with her husband seeking hospitality while she recovered from a migraine, the look Harris exchanged with Stanton was a very speaking one. Neither of them believed the visit was accidental. Nor were they deceived when Mrs Marsham retired to the best guest suite for the rest of the morning and all of the afternoon. Events were to prove them right, for when the stricken lady was asked if she would like her dinner served in her room, she was found to be up and dressing to go downstairs.

The news caused Hugo to dress in his finest, to Stanton's deep alarm. He knew it wasn't like the Earl to go peacocking around unless he had a game little hen in mind, and the Countess's company had never merited all this primping. Hugo's white neckcloth was carefully tied, his silk waistcoat precisely matched the dark-blue of his swallow-tailed coat and his shirt was actually *frilled* at the cuffs. As if that wasn't sign enough that he was dressed to kill, his muscular legs sported knee-breeches and silk stockings.

All this was just as it should be, but Hugo was normally

so contemptuous of old-fashioned notions regarding correct attire that his valet could only view him with the greatest concern and offer what he hoped were subtle words of warning. 'Mr Marsham seems a most devoted husband, my lord.'

Hugo made a minute adjustment to his cravat. 'So he should be.'

'And most protective?' Stanton suggested.

'How the deuce would I know that?'

'It's the way you might find out that worries me!'

'Don't meddle,' Hugo advised him evenly.

'I can't help it, not with the Countess being on the fiery side. She'll come down on you like the heavy cavalry if she gets wind of what you're about tonight. As like as not she'll murder you—and Mrs Marsham, too, for good measure. Don't grin at me like that, neither. I'm speaking the truth, you mark my words.'

'If I am a corpse I will be unable to mark anything, except perhaps the carpet with my gore,' Hugo pointed out.

'There you go, laughing when you should be listening.'

'Oh, stop your damned fussing!' Hugo exclaimed, exasperated. 'I always bring myself off safely, you know that.'

'You've never had the Countess to contend with before.'

Hugo shook back the lace from his cuffs, gave his coat a final tug, and agreed: 'No, I haven't, but I've lived without the spice of danger too long. Quite like the old days, isn't it?'

Stanton, knowing with sinking heart that it was useless to argue with the Earl when he was full of devilment, gave up.

In the Countess's bed-chamber, Harris was only just getting started, for she thought her mistress was about to learn the folly of not sharing her husband's bed.

Dominga was seated before the dressing-table having her hair brushed when Harris began in a colourless tone: 'I have been talking to Mrs Marsham's dresser. A French woman—' she sniffed— 'who dares to look down her foreign nose on anything this side of the Channel. Anyway, I found out that Mrs Marsham will be wearing pink tonight, that being the colour which becomes her best, although I'm not expected to understand such things on account of *only being English!*'

Harris's bosom swelled as she repeated the French dresser's phrase, and indignation put life into her voice as she went on: 'After I'd found out about Mrs Marsham's toilette—and not one word did I breathe about yours, mind!—I told her straight that if Napoleon had *only* had the advantage of *being English* he might be ruling the world as he wanted instead of rotting in exile.'

'Harris, you've never been fighting with Mrs Marsham's maid?' Dominga exclaimed, amused.

'A fine thing it would be if the dresser of an English countess couldn't put a foreign servant in her place,' Harris replied severely.

'Where would I be without you to uphold my dignity?' Dominga wondered wickedly.

'As to that, my lady, there's no saying since you don't always behave as you should. But the point is that I've laid out the red velvet gown you purchased on your last visit to London because Mrs Marsham's pink will never stand against it.'

Dominga looked at her dresser with speculative eyes. How much did she know—or guess? Harris looked back at her impassively, then went on: 'I know you only wear red velvet when you're cross with the Earl and want to provoke him, but it won't do him any harm to be reminded tonight that he's married to a woman of spirit. In fact, it might be just what he needs.'

Dominga guessed then that all her little stratagems had been in vain and that Harris knew, if not everything, a good part of it. She said dryly: 'Very well, I'll wear the red velvet. Have you also decided which jewels I should wear?'

'Just your betrothal ring and the small ruby ear-rings, my lady,' Harris replied, too bent on getting her own way to be put off by irony. 'Mrs Marsham has looks enough, but it's my belief she paints the lily too much.'

Dominga accepted her advice and when she joined Hugo in the Crimson Saloon to await their guests she looked more as if she'd been born into the aristocracy rather than had bought her way in.

The velvet gown had long sleeves which ended in points on the backs of her hands. The neckline tastefully suggested the curves of her breasts, but was wide enough to

reveal nearly all her lovely shoulders. The great ruby
flashed on her hand, tiny rubies trembled from her ears and
her black hair gleamed. She looked like some exotic South-
ern beauty who had strayed into chilly Northern climes and
had unexpectedly bloomed there.

The sight of her caused Hugo a pang. He hadn't tumbled
headlong in love with her as he had with Désirée, but he
had been slowly slipping towards that state, for they were
kindred spirits. Dominga's moods veered as sharply as his
own. She could fire him to passion and anger, and sometimes even melt him to tenderness, but he was a man who
could take only so much frustration. Had she shared his
bed, he might not have been so ready to risk all for another
man's wife. But facts were facts, and Désirée's arrival with
her eyes flashing promises was like putting a present before
an over-excited boy and expecting him not to unwrap it. No
male could go against his nature for ever, and Hugo's
self-discipline was already too sorely tried. If Désirée was
game this evening, then so was he, and the devil take the
rest . . .

Disquiet triumphed for a moment over his recklessness
when he saw that Dominga was wearing red velvet for, like
Harris, he knew she only wore it when she was dressed for
battle. But with whom? He had not upset her. Was it
Désirée she was after and, if so, why? Because she had
learned of his previous marriage plans, or merely because
Désirée's beauty rivalled her own?

Hugo had never believed that caution was the better part
of valour, and he set out deliberately to spike his wife's
guns. 'I've never seen you look more stunning, Dominga,'
he said. 'I'm damned if I won't have you painted in that
gown. You in red velvet will give the gallery just the right
touch of—'

'Gaudiness?' Dominga suggested pleasantly.

'Did it hurt so much?' he asked softly. 'The word I was
thinking of was "colour".'

'How very diplomatic of you. You have hidden qualities—and also, apparently, hidden clothes. Such elegance
would make one think the Princess Charlotte was coming to
dine instead of Mrs Marsham.'

'Ah, but it is for *Mr* Marsham's benefit that I'm rigged up like a tailor's dummy. We don't want him setting it about that we're a pack of dowds down here. Fashion, you will find, is his only topic of conversation, and the only yardstick by which he judges anybody. He's amiable enough, I suppose, and excellent *ton*, but not really my kind of man at all.'

'You're very harsh. Is his wife not your kind of woman, either?'

Hugo eyed her with renewed suspicion and countered: 'You're a female, so you're in a better position to decide what kind of a woman she is.'

'I'm sure I am,' Dominga agreed sweetly, then turned to face the door as their guests arrived.

Désirée floated in on what looked like a cloud of pink, but the smile on her lovely face became a trifle fixed as she glimpsed Dominga in the full glory of her rich velvet. Murderous rage filled her heart as she realised that her thunder had been stolen from her—and this after two full hours of the most meticulous preparation so that she could outshine Hugo's wife!

Désirée would have done better to let her fragile fairness speak for itself, since it was that which had enslaved Hugo in the first place, but she had been unable to resist displaying some of the tricks she had learned in Paris.

Beneath her pink gauze gown, her silk underdress was unmistakably dampened to make it cling to her slender body, and her open-cut silk shoes showed toenails shamelessly tinted with henna. Her hair was tied into a knot on top of her head, from where it fell into bunches of bobbing ringlets over her diamond-decorated ears. More diamonds flashed at her throat, upper and lower arms, hands, and even studded the fan she carried.

Compared to the simple magnificence of her hostess she looked fatally over-dressed and not a little *fast*. Hugo's discerning eyes should have noticed it, but since he felt less like the peacock Stanton had designated him and more like a rutting stag, his blood flamed anew at the sight of her.

Dominga searched Désirée's cheeks, detected rouge cunningly applied there, and said with a knowing smile: 'I see you have quite recovered your colour, *Mrs* Marsham, which must be a great relief to Mr Marsham.'

'Jove, yes!' Augustus responded promptly. 'I've known these migraines lay Désirée low for as much as two days at a time.' He had not realised yet, and probably never would, that his wife was only stricken by this malady when it was convenient to her, and recovered remarkably quickly once her purpose had been served.

He was a regular-featured rather than handsome man and although he was untitled he was connected with some of the finest families in the land. This, coupled with his immense fortune, had given him such an inflated value of his own worth that it simply never occurred to him that men like Hugo regarded him more as an object of ridicule rather than a paragon of excellence to be emulated.

Augustus had reached his early thirties without evincing the slightest interest in anything which happened outside the exclusive circle in which he moved. All his thoughts and energies were concentrated on being a leader of fashion, so that when Désirée had become the rage of Society, she had become his rage, too.

He knew she had once felt a *tendre* for Hugo, but wasn't in the least surprised when she had ultimately recognised his own superior worth, for what female of discrimination would fail to do so? If he was incapable of doting on anybody quite as much as he doted on himself, it genuinely pleased him to grant her every expensive whim, for her beauty brought further attention to himself and she was an incomparable showcase for his wealth.

This evening he had paid his wife the ultimate compliment of choosing his outfit to match hers. Augustus in a pink coat, skin-tight knee-breeches and pink silk stockings was a sight to behold, even without his waistcoat of green watered silk. In addition, a diamond pin nestled among the folds of his neckcloth, a quizzing glass hung from a pink ribbon around his neck, numerous fobs and seals further adorned him, an enamelled snuffbox rested in one lily-white hand and there was enough lace on his shirt to decorate a baby's christening robe.

Augustus, armoured by his vanity, didn't blame Hugo for staring, poor plain fellow that he was, but it was to Dominga that he addressed himself again. 'Gad,' he drawled in his affected way, 'We're all friends here, what?'

Désirée interposed with a superior smile at Dominga: 'Mostly old friends, too, you know.'

'Ah,' Dominga breathed understandingly. 'On the Town a long time before you married, were you?'

Désirée drew in her breath but Augustus, as impervious to insults as he was to the undercurrents of tension in the room, replied roguishly: ''Pon my word, I can't tell you what a dance she led us poor worshippers before she made me the happiest man in the world. Ain't that so, Deversham?'

Hugo bowed and the conversation became general until Jamieson came in to announce that dinner was served. As host, Hugo held out his arm to Désirée and led her through to the dining-room, with Dominga following on Augustus's arm.

During the first course Dominga was unusually quiet, for she was quietly assessing Augustus. He was certainly, as Hugo had said, amiable enough, but with his affected speech and ways, and his total self-absorption, she was forced to the conclusion that here was no jealous husband to aid her in keeping Hugo and Désirée apart. Augustus might frequently raised his quizzing glass to observe things more closely, but he clearly lacked the wit to appreciate what was going on under his very nose.

He beamed benignly on his wife as she chatted gaily about Paris, looked inordinately proud when she flirted with him, and was sublimely unaware that it was Hugo she was really bent on entrancing.

Dominga was not so obtuse, but she thought it hardly likely that Désirée would risk her marriage by doing more than harmlessly dallying with Hugo in public tonight. Her behaviour so far hadn't gone beyond what was socially acceptable, and neither had Hugo's. It would be some time in the future, Dominga thought, that the real risk would come, and in that she erred for she failed to realise that Désirée could be as completely ruthless as she was herself.

Vanity, jealousy and contempt of her husband all combined to make Désirée covet Hugo more than she ever had before. At this moment, to pit herself against his beautiful wife and win meant more to her than all the jewels Augustus had given her. She was that most dangerous of all creatures, the predatory female with something to prove, and Dominga didn't recognise the immediacy of her need. Indeed, quietly counting every glass of champagne her guest drank during and after dinner, Dominga thought with an abstainer's ignorance that it wouldn't be long before she was carried off to bed.

But it was Augustus, a victim of Hugo's finest brandy, who had finally to be helped upstairs, a circumstance which broke up the party. Désirée, Hugo and Dominga bade each other good night and made their separate ways to bed.

Some half-hour later, Dominga lay in her white bed with its scarlet hangings listening to Harris's footsteps receding as she went off to her room. She was glad that she had met Désirée, for she was now able to put a face and a personality to the shadowy figure who had kept her from winning Hugo's love for so long.

Désirée was undeniably beautiful, but blatant enough to have all the makings of a high-class whore. A strong husband like Hugo might have kept her in check, but Augustus would never manage it. Yet if Désirée wished to be sure of keeping her place in Hugo's heart for another year or two, when they would probably judge it safe to resume their *affaire*, she was being her own worst enemy, Dominga thought.

Lusty Hugo surely was, but he was also intelligent and had a certain fastidiousness that Désirée had not made allowances for. He might tumble chambermaids without a second thought, but from women of his own class he expected taste and discretion. He would not for long continue to respect a woman who dampened her under-dresses and painted her nails to bring the attention of rakes upon her, and Dominga was convinced that what Hugo could not respect he could not love.

It was one of the enigmas of his character and the main reason why she, Dominga, had been so long in even winning civility from him. As she closed her eyes for sleep, Dominga smiled. In the long run, she thought, Hugo would come to appreciate the advantage of having a discreet merchant's daughter for a wife rather than a well-bred wanton.

Her smile had scarcely softened in sleep when a hand was

shaking her awake again. 'My lady,' Harris was hissing in her ear. 'The Earl is with Mrs Marsham.'

Harris did not have to repeat her words. They were more than enough to make Dominga sit bolt upright, her mind working with such clarity that sleep might never have claimed it.

'How long have they been together?' she asked.

'Only just,' Harris replied, lighting more candles and holding out a robe for her mistress. 'I had my suspicions, so I hung about instead of going to my room and saw Mrs Marsham's dresser go to fetch my lord. He must have been waiting, for he appeared right away. The maid's gone off to bed, so they're alone together.'

She fetched slippers for Dominga's feet and went on: 'Separate that pair of lovebirds, if that's what they are, but quietly. We don't want any scandal, not before your first season. Mr Marsham's dead to the world, if the snores coming out of his room are anything to go by.'

Dominga stood quite still for a moment, thinking. She was angry that she had underestimated Désirée but, just as her father had always taught her, she sought for a way to turn the situation to her advantage.

The one thing Hugo had always held against her, however unjustified, was what he called her lack of breeding. If she could carry off the coming scene with dignity, and at the same time scorn Désirée into behaving badly, would she not rise in his esteem while Désirée sank?

She thought so. Yes, she really did! Augustus must at all costs be kept out of it, though. If he discovered what was going on he would, as a gentleman, be bound in honour to call Hugo out. Whether it was swords or pistols, Hugo would undoubtedly kill him and then be forced to flee the country. He would have to take Désirée with him, too, to save her from disgrace.

The one that Society would snigger at most would be herself, the innocent party. The knowledge stiffened Dominga in her resolve to act the affronted Countess until Désirée and Hugo squirmed, but to take care in not stirring up a hornets' next while she was doing so.

'Go to bed now,' she ordered Harris. 'You can trust me to be discreet and it's best if you're not mixed up in this. The

Earl will not be too—pleased—to have his little game stopped and he might turn his anger on any witnesses.'

Harris understood that readily enough. She paused only long enough to thrust a lighted candle in its silver holder into Dominga's hand, then hurried away. Her mistress followed her out of the bedroom, but went the other way along the passage.

The principal guest suite had two bedrooms adjoined by dressing-rooms. Dominga paused outside Augustus's door, then, reassured by the uninhibited snores coming from within, passed on to Désirée's. She entered softly, candle aloft, and closed the door as softly behind her.

Désirée and Hugo had not yet got as far as the four-poster. They were on the day-bed and the room was lighted only by the flickering flames of the fire. Hugo, dressed in breeches and with his white shirt open almost to the waist, clasped Désirée to him. Her golden hair was still in ringlets, but they had come free of their ribbons and she wore nothing but a pink nightgown, through which her body gleamed whitely. Her head was thrown back in ecstasy as Hugo kissed her throat. She moved slightly to nibble his ear and, in doing so, saw Dominga.

She gasped as if an avenging demon stood there—and she wasn't far wrong, for Dominga had made a fatal miscalculation. She had come here with her father's brain calmly ticking in her head and telling her how to behave, but she had forgotten that her mother's tempestuous blood also ran in her veins, and she had made no allowance for how she would actually feel when she saw Hugo with another woman in his arms.

She was shaken with rage and pain as fierce as it was unexpected. All this time she had seen Hugo as an object of her revenge and never as a real man at all, but she saw him so now and reacted as a woman scorned.

All her calm logic disappeared in a red mist of fury. Murder filled her eyes. Everything, including the need not to disturb Augustus, was forgotten as she put down the candle on a table and advanced on the entwined couple.

Désirée gasped again, with very real fear, so that at last Hugo was forced to stop exploring her perfumed skin with his lips, albeit reluctantly, and raise his head to look at her. Frowning, he turned to follow her stricken gaze and saw his wife bearing down on them.

Magnificent as she looked in her filmy white *négligé* and with her black hair loose to her waist, there was a wildness about her that caused Hugo to pull Désirée protectively against him.

If Dominga had needed a spark to fire her rage, that instinctive movement of his would have provided it. Utterly out of control, she went for him with such strength that instead of pulling him away from Désirée, they both tumbled from the day-bed on to the floor.

Hugo released Désirée and she rolled clear as he caught his wife's clawing hands and jerked her down on top of him. She struggled so fiercely that it was all he could do to hold her and they wrestled over the floor, locked in a grim struggle for supremacy.

Désirée tried to stand up, found her legs would not support her, and huddled whimpering against the day-bed. 'For God's sake stop it,' she moaned. 'You'll waken Augustus and ruin us all.'

Neither took any notice, nor even heard her. Hugo was trying to subdue his wife by pinning down her writhing body with his own and she was resisting with unabated fury. Finally, however, her strength gave out and she lay still. Hugo's weight was all but crushing her and there was nothing more she could do to stop him forcing her hands down to the floor and holding them there. Each was panting and for long seconds they just glared at each other.

Hugo's fair hair was dampened with sweat where it fell across his forehead. His face was unmarked, but she had ripped his shirt and scored heavily with her nails across his chest. Dominga saw the scar he had carried since Waterloo and wished savagely that whoever had wielded that sword had struck with a truer hand.

Her breasts rose and fell as she struggled for breath, her cheeks were flushed, her eyes still wild and her black hair tangled about her.

'Damned alley cat,' Hugo muttered, not daring to let her go.

'The only alley cat in this room,' she gasped, 'is Mrs

Marsham. You should know that, with your penchant for playing the Tom.'

His hands tightened cruelly on her wrists. 'I'm target enough for you, Dominga. Leave Désirée out of this.'

'How very noble of you, but quite unnecessary,' she retorted. 'Women who behave as Mrs Marsham does are usually quite capable of defending themselves.'

'Don't sneer at Désirée. She is a lady.'

'Oh?' Dominga's eyebrows rose scornfully. 'Is she setting an example that you wish me to follow, then?'

'Stop it!' Hugo ordered, leaning more heavily on her as if to crush the spirit out of her.

Dominga winced but gasped defiantly: 'I will not stop it. What lady cuckolds her husband while she is still a bride? It's all of a piece with dampening her underdress and painting her nails. She'll be tying her garter in public next.'

Her words struck home. Hugo turned his head from her and looked at Désirée. He saw her not as she had been last summer but as she was now, a fast matron he would be ashamed to call his wife.

Désirée read his look and whispered: 'It is only because I love you, Hugo . . .'

'What kind of love demands the risks you have made Hugo take tonight?' Dominga demanded. 'He could be fighting a duel tomorrow and then fleeing the country, having to abandon everything he has worked so hard to save. You call that love? I call it vanity.'

Dominga was at last giving part of her prepared speech. She wished as passionately as ever to win Hugo from Désirée and her rage was sufficiently spent for her to realise how badly she had blundered. She must not let the wild side of her be her undoing, as it had been her mother's.

For answer, Désirée began to cry, sure that it would make Hugo bundle his mad wife from the room and come to comfort her. But Hugo loathed tears and thought that if anybody had the right to cry it was his wife.

He looked down at her and asked: 'Have you done fighting?'

'Since I cannot win, yes.'

'Ah, Dominga,' he said, smiling a little, 'you always say

and do the unexpected. I've never appreciated you enough, have I?'

As always when he was tender with her, Dominga did not know what to say. She was not going to make the same mistake as Désirée and cry, so she endured the painful ache in her throat and answered gruffly: 'You could begin by releasing me. I can scarcely breathe and I must be black and blue all over.'

He freed her hands and rolled off her. He sat up as she did, took her wrists and rubbed the circulation back into them gently, then raised them to his lips and kissed them.

'I wouldn't have hurt you for the world,' he told her, 'but you gave me precious little choice.'

The touch of his lips on her wrists had done terrible, weakening things to her. She smiled at him a little mistily. 'I didn't, did I? I think I must have bad blood in me, Hugo.'

'Not you. The bad blood's all mine.' He touched her cheek with gentle fingers, adding with unusual awkwardness: 'You're a good sort of girl, Dominga, and I'm a devil of a fellow. I'll try to be better in future, though, I promise you.'

A gasp, this time of outrage, came from Désirée. She had been frightened, humiliated, ignored and scorned, but witnessing Hugo courting his wife was beyond the bounds of her endurance. She said icily: 'When you've *quite* finished, I wish you would go away. I never want to see either of you again. Ever!'

Hugo helped Dominga to her feet then went over to help Désirée to hers, saying: 'We were fools to think marriage would change nothing between us, Désirée. Everything is changed, and ourselves most of all, but let's part friends for old times' sake.' He bowed over her hand and kissed it.

It was beautifully done, and Dominga at least had the grace to acknowledge it as he took her own hand and led her from the room. She could scarcely dare to breathe. She had done everything wrong, lost her temper and provoked an undignified scene, yet in some strange way she had annihilated her rival in the process. And she thought, as she walked along the passage with Hugo, that of all three of them she was the biggest fool of all.

It was with love that she had been pursuing Hugo all this

time, though she had called it revenge because anything else would have shamed her proud and wounded spirit. By telling herself she hated him, she had given herself a reason for hunting him down. The truth was—had always been—that she simply could not stay away from him. The ten golden guineas had been her one precious link with him, which was why she had hoarded them so carefully and stared at them so often. She did not know what she would do with them now. She only knew she could not destroy him without also destroying herself.

All these were chastening and novel thoughts, so that when they stopped outside her bed-chamber she could not look at him. He put a finger under her chin and tipped up her face to his. 'I would never have gone to her if you had been a proper wife to me,' he murmured, his finger moving caressingly along the line of her chin.

She felt as shy as a schoolgirl and almost as tongue-tied. 'I—I only have your word for that,' she stammered.

His finger was lightly outlining her full lips now, so that they began to tremble, and her heart began to beat with an ache so fierce she almost cried out against it. 'And yet,' she heard him say, 'bad as I am, haven't you always found my word good? Look at me, Dominga, and answer me.'

Dominga looked at him, and was lost. There was just enough moonlight shining through the great window at this end of the passage for her to see, or perhaps merely to guess at, his features. It really didn't matter, for even if it had been pitch black she still could have conjured up every line of his much-loved face.

'Y-yes,' she admitted. 'I can trust your word.'

Very slowly, very gently, he pulled her to him until she nestled in the circle of his arms. 'Then do you think you can trust me to love you as you should be loved? As I would have loved you from the beginning if it hadn't have been for Désirée? I'm free of her now, Dominga, and I love you in so many more ways than I ever loved her.'

She melted against him, all her barriers down, eager only to accept his love and give hers without any reservations at all. His arms tightened about her. He bent to kiss her dark hair, and murmured against it: 'Release me from my promise, Dominga.'

She very nearly cried, she was so swamped with love for him, and it was all she could do to whisper shakily: 'I think I already have.'

'Darling . . .' He swept her into his arms and carried her through to her bed-chamber, kicking the door shut behind him so violently that the sound echoed up the empty passage.

'Hush,' Dominga cautioned, as if she were about to be caught in a guilty act herself. 'You'll wake up the entire household.'

'If you couldn't do it with all the fuss you made, a slim chance I'd stand,' Hugo retorted, laying her on the bed and joining her without ever releasing her from his grip.

He kissed her, then, and the world receded for both of them until Dominga felt compelled to say: 'Hugo, you still have your boots on.'

His own particular imp of mischief made him answer: 'Désirée didn't complain.'

She struck out at him, but he was expecting it. He laughed and caught her hand, kissing it. 'Oh, Dominga, won't you believe that she means nothing to me any more? If she did, I couldn't even mention her. Surely you see that?'

She did, but still had to ask: 'You're certain I'm the one you truly want?'

Hugo had no intention of talking the night away and so he silenced her doubts with kisses. No further questions occurred to her and she was beyond caring about the answers, anyway, for she was responding to the sure touch of his hands and lips as completely as she had in the inn at Chersey two endless years ago. But this time there was love combined with his passion, for he was telling her so all the time, and it caused her more exultation than ever revenge could have done.

She fell asleep, finally, on his chest and they were still in each other's arms when Harris came in at dawn, as was her custom, to prepare her mistress for riding. She crossed the room to pull back the curtains, glanced over her shoulder at the bed, then hurriedly drew them together again.

Hugo and Dominga had never got around to drawing the scarlet drapes about the four-poster, and even Harris's hard heart, once she had recovered from her surprise, was touched to see them lying so lovingly together.

She crept from the room, closed the door softly behind her, and held her fingers to her lips as she saw Stanton approaching to enter the Earl's room. As he stopped beside her, she whispered: 'We're not needed yet, and they'll not be riding out this morning.' Seeing his eyes widen, she explained: 'They're in bed together.'

'You're sure it's the Countess he has with him?' Stanton asked.

'Of course I am,' Harris hissed. 'It's her bed they're in.'

A wide smile spread over Stanton's homely features. 'And about time, too,' he said.

'That's none of our business,' Harris reminded him, then showed a rare glimpse of her human side by adding with considerable satisfaction: 'That's Mrs Marsham's nose put properly out of joint—and her dresser's too. It's an ill wind, Stanton . . .'

'Indeed it is,' he agreed, and they went downstairs to enjoy a pot of tea and their unexpected leisure.

Dominga did not awaken until some two hours after that, and she was as full of love when she opened her eyes as when she had closed them. She propped herself up on her elbow and looked with adoration at her sleeping husband. This satisfied her for some minutes, then she began to crave the feel of his arms round her again, and his kisses, and to hear him reaffirm his love for her.

She played with the hairs on his chest and, when this failed to wake him, gently kissed the marks she had made with her nails when she had been so furious with him. It was hard to remember that fury now and she smiled as she raised her head to brush her lips across his.

Hugo stirred. 'Désirée . . .' he murmured sleepily. 'Darling, darling Désirée . . .'

CHAPTER
SIXTEEN

ANGUISH seared through Dominga, a hurt so acute that it took her breath away. It was as if she had fallen from heaven to hell in the space of seconds. She could not believe that twice she had given her whole heart to this man, and twice it had been returned unwanted. It was only her body he had a use for and she, who had vowed she would never be fooled by him again, had trusted him.

She stared down at him, despising herself for her weakness and hating him for the skilful way he played upon it. It had been Désirée he'd wanted all the time last night but, foiled, had charmed her into becoming a substitute.

Dominga's face flamed with chagrin. She had been duped, there was no other word for it. That she, who was rich and beautiful and thought herself so clever, could be reduced to a gullible, fawning woman was more than her pride could bear. She'd been his for no more than a few soft words and a pretence of love.

Amazement at her own stupidity drove her hurt deep down inside her, where it was wrapped protectively in rage. She did not know how to crawl into a corner and cry. She only knew how to fight.

Hugo stirred again. His eyes did not open, but his betraying arms came round her shoulders and he pulled her sleepily down on to his chest.

That did it. She wrenched herself free and with clenched fists began to rain blows on his head and shoulders.

'What the deuce . . .' Hugo came awake feeling as if the hounds of hell had been loosed on him. He managed to grab one of her flailing arms before he even realised what was happening, and felt teeth sink into his wrist. He swore, released her and rolled to the far side of the bed.

Dominga scrambled to the bedside table, snatched the heavy candelabrum and raised it to strike him. Wide awake now, he twisted it from her grasp and hurled it away. 'Have you gone mad?' he shouted.

With burning eyes and only her long black hair to cover her nakedness, Dominga did indeed look more like a wild woman than a Countess, but she screamed back at him: 'Last night I was mad, but I have come to my senses now. You're despicable! A worse rogue than ever ended on the gallows! But I am your Nemesis, Hugo, and I'll make you pay and pay again for your duplicity.'

He stared blankly at her. 'But—' helplessly he indicated the bed, her nakedness and his own—'last night we . . .'

'I know what we did last night!' she screeched, unable to bear being reminded of it. She leaped off the bed, grabbed up her flimsy robe and pulled it on. 'Last night I believed you. This morning I know your lies for what they are. You couldn't have Désirée and so you settled for me, you *animal!*'

'That's not true . . .' he began, but he was not allowed to finish.

'Isn't it?' she spat at him. 'Then whose name did you speak in your sleep? *Hers!*'

'Oh, my god,' he groaned.

'You don't have a god, only a devil. Use his name if you wish, not that his aid will save you. "Trust me", you said, and I did—just like the last time. That I could be so imbecilic!'

'Last time?' he repeated dazedly.

'Oh, yes, there was a last time.' She went to her dressing-table, kicking his breeches out of the way as she did so, and unlocked her jewellery box. She flung away the top tray with its precious contents, grabbed the silk purse from beneath, and turned to face him.

'Do you remember that day at Chersey when you proposed to me? You thought then that you had seen me before and, by heaven, you had! All of me! I *was* that chambermaid you seduced. I never had a bastard half-sister, as I told you. Did you, in your arrogance, believe you were the only one who could lie and cheat? If you think you scored a great victory over me last night, now you know what a hollow one it was.'

'You were that over-hot little handful?' Hugo couldn't

take it in. 'But you could never have been a chambermaid!'

She held up the purse and shook it as she advanced on him, so that the coins inside jingled. 'Then how did I come by this bounty, unless for services rendered? You have been tricked into marrying a woman you once used as a wanton. How great is your precious pride now? I happened to be in the village two years ago when you and your brother put up at the inn. Molly, the real chambermaid, told me about the young milords who were staying and I—heaven help me!—was curious enough to want to see you, so I pretended to be a chambermaid as well. Do you need to be reminded of what happened next?'

'Harry and I tossed for you,' he breathed, 'and I won.'

'Yes, you won,' she agreed bitterly, 'but who wins now?'

'I—it's not possible.'

She looked down at him contemptuously, then opened the purse and spilled the ten shining guineas over him. 'These say it is. I waited and I planned and finally I purchased you. My pride was salvaged. I always meant to grind yours into the dust and I'm sure I have succeeded.'

He was quiet for a long time, gathering the coins together and toying with them, but absent-mindedly, as if he was unaware of what he was doing. Then he said: 'You spoke nothing of revenge last night.'

'I—' Words choked her. How could she explain that last night revenge seemed worthless, and that she would have willingly given all she possessed in exchange for his love? She swallowed and began again: 'Last night is over. This morning is the time of reckoning.'

'And you expect to collect some dues from me?' Hugo patted the empty space beside him where she had lain in ecstasy such a short time ago. 'Yet you were willing enough here, and two years ago I never raped you.'

'No, you seduced me, but I was only fifteen and—' her voice filled with self-scorn— 'I trusted you. In my ignorance I expected love, not money.'

'I see. It was me you wanted all the time, then, not my title?'

'That, too,' she retorted proudly. 'I wasn't born to be a *Mrs* like your darling Désirée.'

His eyes were quite unreadable as he asked: 'What if

Harry had lived? How then would you have got your title *and* your revenge?'

'I'd have married him and driven you mad with desire for me. You have your own curious honour, Hugo. I believe you would seduce any woman without a second thought— save your brother's wife. Yet I would have succeeded in making you betray him and you'd have spent the rest of your life despising yourself.'

'You're as much a devil as I am,' he said through white lips.

She shrugged. 'One is only as good as the company one keeps. Understand this, dear husband. You have used me for the last time. In future it will be you who is used. You will never touch me again unless it pleases me. *Me!*' She stretched out her hand and touched his tousled hair mockingly. 'Probably you want me again already. A pity, for I want only my breakfast.'

His eyes blazed, so that at last she had a glimpse of how much punishment she had inflicted on him in her turn. She felt coldly triumphant, but all the same it seemed prudent to put herself out of his reach. As she passed his breeches on the floor, she picked them up and tossed them to him. 'Go away now. I'll let you know when you may come in here again.'

She reached her dressing-table, took up one of her gold-backed brushes and began to brush her hair, as if his presence was of no more importance to her than a servant's. She was still buoyed up by rage but, as she watched him covertly, she could not help thinking how different things might have been if only he had proved worthy of her trust.

For some time he did not move, but lay back among the pillows weighing the coins in his hand and staring at her. Then with an abrupt movement he swung himself out of bed and pulled on his breeches. As he stood up, she reminded him contemptuously: 'Your boots, my lord.'

'Those, my lady, will be left for your maid to find,' he replied evenly, and came towards her so purposefully that she backed away in alarm. He looked powerfully masculine in only his breeches and she distrusted the dangerous glitter in his eyes.

'Hugo,' she said sharply. 'Go away or I shall call my maid.'

'The whole household wouldn't be able to stand between you and me just now,' he answered softly. 'Did you really think to see me grovel before you? Your misfortune, *dear wife*, is that you are tied to me and not Harry. I don't doubt you could have trampled all over him, but I am not so— tame!'

He reached out and grabbed her wrist, for she was backed up against the dressing-table and could retreat no more. He opened her hand and thrust the guineas back into it, closing her fingers round them and holding them there cruelly.

She winced. 'What are you doing?'

He released her hand so that the guineas fell from her nerveless fingers to the floor, grasped her by the arm and began to drag her towards his room. 'By god, I warned you not to play dangerous games with me, but it seems you still have to learn who is master here.'

She threw herself down, thinking that would stop him. It didn't. He dragged her on until she grabbed hold of a leg of her day-bed, pulling him up short. He reached down, forced her hand away and tossed her over his shoulder like a sack of hay.

'Let me go!' she screamed, pounding at him with her fists and feet, but he seemed to be made of iron. Just when Dominga thought she was lost, the door opened and Harris came in. The maid stopped short, her dignity for once unequal to the situation. Her mouth dropped open.

'Harris!' Dominga shrieked. 'Save me!'

Hugo swung round and roared: 'Out!'

Harris fled. Hugo strode through the adjoining dressing-rooms with his madly struggling burden and into his bed-room. Stanton was engaged in neatly setting out his clothes for the day.

'Out!' Hugo roared again.

The sight of the Earl with his Countess over his shoulder, and both scarcely clad, might have been an everyday occurrence, for the expression on Stanton's face did not change. 'Certainly, my lord,' he replied, and bowed. Then, like the veteran of Wellington's campaigns in the Peninsula that he was, he beat an orderly and strategic retreat.

'Oh, how dare you!' Dominga cried, almost sobbing with humiliation. 'Put me down, you beast!'

'Beast am I now? You called me softer names last night, my love.'

'I am not your love!' She gasped as she found herself dumped on a chair by Hugo's dressing-table, and stared as he pulled out one drawer after another, rummaging through them. 'In heaven's name, what are you doing?'

'Since it cost you one hundred thousand guineas to purchase me, my getting your services for ten guineas a time is too good a bargain to pass up. I don't generally have much need of ready cash, but there must be some here somewhere. Ah!' He found a box, snatched some coins from it and thrust them into her hand. 'For last night,' he went on. 'I like to pay my way, and you shall have ten more shortly.' He began to drag her to his great bed, not even flinching as the coins she flung at him bounced off his arms and chest.

Dominga kicked him, but her feet were bare and she only hurt herself. She managed to throw an arm around one of the elaborately-carved bedposts and clung to it grimly.

He shook his head at her. 'You're only wasting time. You know you can't fight me.'

'And you can't rape me,' she said through clenched teeth. 'You might think you can, but you can't. You'd loathe yourself for taking an unwilling woman.'

'But wasn't that an object of your revenge—to make me loathe myself?'

She swore.

'Are you sure you only masqueraded as a chambermaid?' he asked. 'You seem very well acquainted with the language of the stables.'

'Mock me if you wish, but I still maintain your pride won't allow you to ravish a reluctant woman.'

'Oh, you wouldn't be reluctant for long.'

'I hate you,' she whispered.

His eyes hardened. 'If I believed that . . . if I really believed that . . . you'd never have to fear my touch again. But I think you love me, Dominga, and I mean to make you admit it.'

'Love!' she yelled as he freed her from the bedpost. 'You call this love? This—this despicable bullying of a helpless woman.'

'Appealing to my better nature?' He laughed and picked her up, carrying her the last few steps. 'Alas, Dominga, I don't have one. What will you try next? Tears?'

'I wouldn't give you the satisfaction,' she vowed.

'No, of course you wouldn't. You'd see me in hell first.' She found herself being set back on her feet and hugged. 'Just as I'd see you in hell before I let you crow over me. What a pair we are. I think we must have been born for each other, my darling.'

She leaned against his chest because she had no choice, and her legs felt so weak that she was sure she would have fallen but for his supporting arms. She was stunned, too, by his change of tactics. She could only wait for her heart to stop thudding so violently and pray for her strength and wits to return.

Hugo kissed her hair, murmuring tenderly: 'Ah, Dominga, why did you never listen when I warned you against pushing me too far?'

Dominga knew the immediate threat was over, but she was warier than ever. He was using a new weapon now, tenderness, correctly judging it to be more effective against her than rage or violence. But not this time. She asked stonily: 'Are you going to let me go?'

'Not until you tell me that you love me.'

'Then we shall be here all day.'

'All week, all month, all year if necessary.'

He sounded so determined she had to believe him, yet every moment she spent in his arms like this weakened her and he, the clever devil, knew it. She had to get away from him somehow, and so she said: 'You forget that we have guests. Désirée will not want to spend another night here, but she and Augustus cannot go without first taking leave of us.'

'You're a cunning minx,' he applauded, 'but you'll not escape me that way. I don't give a damn about the Marshams.'

'Naturally not. You are the great Earl of Deversham and therefore above concerning yourself with the finer points of hospitality. If you did that, there's no telling where it might end. You might even be forced to recognise the impropriety of seducing a guest while her husband sleeps next door.'

Hugo's self-control slipped a little. His hands came up to her shoulders and he shook her. 'Watch what you're about. I take as little to ridicule as I do to revenge.'

'Must I hold my tongue for fear of violence?' she retorted. 'You'd best carry out whatever fiendish plans you have for me, then, because I'll be *damned* if I'll be cowed by you.'

His face cleared and he laughed and caught her to him again. 'Darling Dominga, I wouldn't have missed knowing you for the world. And to think I believed civilian life would be a bore. I'd have sold out with an easier mind if I'd known what delights you held in store for me.'

Her bosom heaved. 'It pleases you to ridicule me, now!'

'I'm not ridiculing you, I'm *appreciating* you. Don't you know a compliment when you hear it? I've never paid a finer one to any woman, I promise you.'

'I distrust your promises, and your compliments, and everything about you.'

'Now that's a pity, because I haven't the patience to ride on the curst roundabout of your imagained wrongs again.'

'Imagined!' Dominga expostulated.

'Well, magnified. Is it so hard to accept me as I am and love me?' Hugo ran his hands over her back in a possessive way that sent shivers right down to her toes.

'Don't do that!' She gritted her teeth until his hands obediently stopped, terrified of the response he evoked in her. It seemed there was no part of her that wasn't vulnerable to his touch. She drew in her breath and tried another tack. 'You surprise me, my lord. I thought the things I told you would have given you an abhorrence of me for life.'

He bent his head and kissed her neck, his lips seeming to scorch her flesh. Then he rubbed his cheek against hers and murmured: 'I've despised, distrusted, resented and even on occasion hated you, but all that's gone now. There's only love left and I offer it to you as a far more satisfying form of revenge.'

'Oh!' Dominga's throat tightened. She ached to believe him, but dared not. 'How can you say you love me when you wake with Désirée's name on your lips?'

She was shaken again as Hugo's self-control slipped a little further. 'I'll be damned if I'll spend the rest of my life paying for a mistake I made when I wasn't even conscious,' he snapped. 'Hell's bells, Dominga, what are you trying to do? Drive me into Bedlam?'

'Nonetheless, speaking her name proved how treacherous you are.'

'All it proved, you idiot, is that old habits die hard.' He picked her up and put her into his bed. As she tried to scramble out, he ordered: 'Stay there. I won't harm you. You're quite safe until you tell me that you love me and then, I think, you won't wish to be so safe any more.'

'But if you're not going to . . . what . . . why must I stay here?'

He climbed in beside her, pulled her into his arms and put her head on his shoulder. 'Because I know you better than you know yourself. You won't be able to lie with me like this and still resist me.'

'Damn your arrogance,' she breathed, and started to struggle.

He held her head tightly against his shoulder. 'Be still.'

Dominga subsided, but she was angry enough to be sure she could be every bit as resolute as he was.

Time passed. His arms remained firmly around her, but he did not speak. It had its effect, for eventually she said: 'Hugo?'

'Yes?'

'How long do I have to endure this punishment?'

'Comfort yourself with the knowledge that you're not suffering half as much as I am. To deny lust to prove love is worse than purgatory.'

Dominga said no more for a while, then found she was quite unconsciously playing with the hairs on his chest. She pulled her hand away as if it had betrayed her.

'Pity,' Hugo sighed. 'I was enjoying that.'

She stiffened but, as more time passed, a most delicious languor crept over her. It was nice to be snuggled against him like this, and nothing would have been more natural than to say 'Hugo, I love you', and leave the future to fend for itself.

But that, of course, was what he wanted and what she could not do. Never again would she be able to hold his arrogance in check if she succumbed now. She would only have encouraged him to become more insufferable than ever.

The problem was that the more time that passed, the less insufferable he became. It was so terribly hard to remember that his tenderness was turned on merely to defeat her. She must get away from him, and quickly, but how? And then it came to her, the one trick she still had left to play.

'What diabolical plot are you hatching now?' Hugo asked conversationally.

'No plot,' she answered icily. 'I have decided to tell you the whole truth about myself.'

He ruffled her hair. 'If you mean to shock me by saying you knew other men between myself at Chersey and now, you're wasting your breath. Casanova himself couldn't have sidetracked you from your revenge, thank god.'

'Not that kind of truth. You held up your nose at my father because he was in commerce, did you not? Well, my mother was no Spanish gentlewoman. She was a gipsy. A common gipsy.'

'Was she now?' Hugo sounded entirely unconcerned.

Dominga was stunned. She twisted within his grasp and scrambled to her knees, so that she could look down into his face.

'Pray pull your gown together,' he pleaded. 'I'm not made of stone, and my flesh is weaker than most.'

She clutched her gown about her breasts, but it was more a reflex action than anything. 'Didn't you hear what I said? My mother was a *gipsy*.'

'I couldn't care less if she was Hottentot,' he replied evenly.

The world reeled about her, for nothing made sense any more. She sank back on her heels and stammered: 'But— but you had your lawyers check my background most meticulously. My father had concealed the truth too cleverly for them to find out, but it *is* the truth! I am what you originally thought. A money-grubbing vulgarian. You *must* despise me now!'

'Certainly I would, if I didn't love you so,' he agreed.

'Hugo,' she said, and her voice broke. 'You *cannot* love me.'

He sighed. 'I wish I could break you of this dreadful habit you have of telling me what I may and may not do.'

'Don't tease me,' she pleaded. 'I—I just don't understand you—or—or anything.'

'Then perhaps we're making some progress at last,' he said, smiling at her in a manner that made her very bones melt. He traced her lips with one finger in a way that was becoming sweetly familiar, and went on: 'Next you'll realise there is nothing you can say that will shock or shame me out of loving you.'

'But you would never had married me had you known!'

'No, but now that I have I'm past redemption. It's of no importance to me how many skeletons you have in your family closet, so long as you don't rattle them too often.' He smiled in that special way again, and added: 'Shut your mouth, Dominga. Gaping doesn't become you.'

She snapped her mouth shut. He laughed and pulled her down to his shoulder. 'Back you come, for it's clear you have some more thinking to do. I wonder what in thunder you will come up with next?'

'Aren't you afraid somebody else will find out about me?'

'Why should I be? Anybody who dared to criticise my Countess would have too short a time to live to be worth bothering about.'

'Hugo, your arrogance!' she exclaimed, awed.

'Magnificent, isn't it? Is that why you love me?'

'I haven't said I do.' All the same, she snuggled against his shoulder as if she belonged there. 'Besides, you can't possibly respect me after all I've told you, and where's the love without respect?'

'Any girl who gets herself seduced at fifteen then schemes with diabolical cunning to trap her seducer into giving her a wedding band is worthy of the devil's own respect,' he answered promptly.

'Perhaps,' she said huskily, 'you're not such a devil after all.'

'Alas, no. You have the wild beast tamed, Dominga.'

She gave an unladylike snort. 'If I believed that I'd be as mad as a March hare.'

'Hares are only mad when they are courting, darling, and I don't see that people are any different. I'll swear that, one way or another, I've been half out of my mind ever since I married you.'

'But you never courted me,' she pointed out.

'An error I'm doing my best to make up for.' His hand slid down her arm from her shoulder and crept around her waist.

She held it there to stop it straying any farther while she asked: 'What if I did say I loved you and then—then—you still awoke murmuring Désirée's name?'

'You may beat me.'

'And go through all this again?' she exclaimed wrathfully.

'Is it so awful? I can't think when I've ever been happier. It's a wonderful thing, holding the woman I love in my arms, even if she does happen to be an artful, low-born hussy.'

'A fitting mate, then, for the descendant of robber barons!'

'For god's sake leave my ancestors out of this or we really will be here all year,' he advised her.

'Would that be so awful,' she mocked, 'if you really loved me?'

'If!' Hugo hauled her up beside him on the pillows, his patience worn out, and kissed her with such lingering sweetness that the last of her doubts melted away.

'Oh!' she gasped. 'Hugo, I think I am going to cry.'

'No, you're not. You're going to kiss me back.'

'See!' she exclaimed furiously. 'One moment of weakness from me and already you're telling me what to do.'

'So help me, Dominga, if you won't be quiet I really will murder you.'

She saw that the wild glint was back in his blue eyes, the eyes that had haunted her for so long, and gave a sigh of sheer happiness. 'I love you, Hugo,' she said.

'At last,' he breathed, and moved to kiss her, but she held him off by placing her hand across his lips.

'Just a minute, Hugo.'

'Darling, I don't have another *moment*!' But he saw that she was looking serious and so he tried to content himself by gently nibbling her fingers.

'I just wanted to say . . . ask . . . well, it will always be like this in between, won't it?'

Hugo frowned. 'In between what?'

'Us fighting.'

'Good god, woman, I'm not trying to fight you!'

'No, not now, but you'll find a reason soon enough, or I will. We're not—peaceful—people, Hugo, and never will be. It will be all right, though, won't it, if we can be loving like this when we are not quarrelling?'

'It will be wonderful,' he promised her, and moved her hand aside so that he could kiss away for ever all the pain and humiliation he had caused her.

Dominga wound her arms around his neck and kissed him back so that he, in his turn, forgot he had ever loved a fairer and more fragile beauty.

'To think that I have all this and a coronet, too,' Dominga murmured ecstatically against his lips.

He raised his head and looked at her. 'What did you say?'

'Only that I loved you, Hugo.'

But he had heard her and he said wickedly: 'And I love you, too. Now which one are you? Ah, yes. Dominga . . .'

She beat at him with her fists, but he only laughed and took his punishment until he was able to persuade her once more round to loving him.

Your chance to step into the past and re-live four love stories...

TAKE
FOUR BOOKS
FREE

An introduction to
The Masquerade Reader Service.

NO OBLIGATION.